Enchanted Youth

RICHIE McMULLEN

*This book is dedicated to
every boy who has been
or is currently involved
in any form of prostitution.*

First published May 1990 by
GMP Publishers Ltd,
P O Box 247,
London N17 9QR

World Copyright © 1990 Richie J.McMullen

Distributed in North America by
Alyson Publications Inc.,
40 Plympton St, Boston, MA 02118, USA

Distributed in Australia by Stilone Pty Ltd.,
P O Box 155, Broadway, NSW 2007, Australia

British Library Cataloguing in Publication Data

McMullen, Richie
    Enchanted Youth.
    1. Male homosexuals. Prostitution – Biographies
    I. Title
    306.743092

 ISBN 0-85449-134-1

Printed and bound in the E C on environmentally-friendly paper by
Norhaven A/S, Viborg, Denmark.

Enchanted Youth

Running Away

I had three assets when I stepped on to the train at Liverpool's Lime Street Station that cold November morning in 1958; my body, my mind and the clothes I stood up in. My body was fifteen years old, excited, eager for the unknown and ready for all the sex and money it could come by. My body pulsed energy which my mind had difficulty dealing with in harmony. I was a boy out of balance. My mind belonged to a child and an old man, all at the same time. More than anything else in the world my body wanted love and my mind demanded answers to the questions which tormented me and which always began with 'why?'.

I carried my fragile assets to an empty compartment, with the same precise care that the other passengers carried their luggage, and arranged them proudly facing the engine. I had no bags, no money and a head full of dreams of what might be. I couldn't have been happier. My pockets, other than for my one-way ticket, were empty. I'd carried nothing from the house I was all too glad to leave. I'd have gone naked, like Saint Francis, if it were possible. Of all the saints I'd learnt about at school, Saint Francis was my all time favourite. I mean, here was a guy any inner city boy could identify with. A guy who stole cloth from his rich father to pay for the materials to rebuild a church. A right scally who did what he felt he had to. Then, when his father twigged and got the law in, Frannie stepped out of his clothes and gave them back to his father and went off bollock naked into the unknown to do his own thing. That's what I call a gutsy kind of fella, know what I mean?

I had more than Saint Frannie, didn't I? I mean, I had a train ticket to London and a decent set of clothes. But I wasn't going to build any church! Liverpool, and for all I knew, every other city, was stuffed full of churches. All of them packed out and all demanding money from the poor bastards who were hooked on the addictive messages preached at them every Sunday. *'Give now and get your reward in heaven.'* If God, whose very existence I was becoming to seriously doubt, wanted to rebuild his church, then he sure was getting the message across in a cock-eyed kind of way. The best fed, best housed and best dressed people in post-war Liverpool were the priests. My young mind saw no justice in any of it. The church had been built and rebuilt so often that the years ahead would see many turned into bingo halls and workshops.

There were enough churches! I had a life to build and the only means available were my mind and body. I put my feet up on the seat opposite and cursed my mind for once again allowing a prayer to Saint Francis to invade my consciousness. Why did I say those stupid prayers? Perhaps, because I was a first generation English boy who thought himself to be totally Irish. Or, perhaps because there were times when aged twelve or so, when I wanted to please my Wexford born mother by becoming the priest she prayed for. Perhaps, too, because I was riddled with guilt about the sex I'd had with Pip at school, with men in public toilets, in cinemas, the backs of cars, behind bushes and every other damn place. I'd have to watch for the signals, you know, when the prayers start to come and change things in my head; think of something different. This was a technique I'd already developed to get rid of those erections which always came up when most unwanted. I used to think about being examined by the school doctor, who was a fat, old woman. It always worked, well, nearly always.

Why is it that boys always get an erection just as they have to get off the bus, or when the teacher tells them to stand up straight, or when they're trying to have a piss? And why is it that the erection always seems to know precisely where the opening in their underpants is? Popping through, forcing itself against the front of their trousers?

My thoughts were rudely interrupted when the guard opened the carriage door, slid into the compartment, like a snake, and told me, in one long drawn out hissing breath – of the adult man whose seen it all before – to take my feet off the seat, produce my ticket and have some respect for other people's property. Why is it that a boy in this situation happens to have an erection and can't find his ticket? With one hand trying like hell to cover the bulge I knew he'd seen and the other searching the otherwise empty pockets for the lost ticket; I couldn't find it! The train was still standing in the station, the guard beginning to move, in his snake-like rhythm, from one foot to the other with increasing impatience. He was ready to show me his fangs, poison me with his venom, and I couldn't find the ticket which took me all the money I had to purchase.

'Have you actually got a ticket or not? You either have or you haven't, which is it?' He hissed.

Why is it that adults who wear uniforms all seem to sound the same?

'Of course I've got a ticket, what do you take me for?'

'Then would you mind letting me see it, please?'

Why did his *please* sound like, 'I know you haven't got a ticket and I'm just about to throw you off my train you smart arsed scally'? I had no choice, the erection wouldn't go down and I had to stand up to search my back pockets. Stuff it, be proud, if you've got it then show it off. I stood up and faced the guard, my erection sticking out for all to see. He looked at me, at the erection, back at me in shocked disbelief, and then looked away in embarrassment. I had him! He was embarrassed! The boot was on the other foot now. I enjoyed watching the snake mutate into a worm, looking for an escape route. No proud fangs showing now.

The ticket was wedged under the flap of my back pocket, I pulled it loose, as slowly and as casually as I could, hesitated, and then showed it to the transformed worm. He clipped it quickly, eager to crawl beneath the nearest stone, whilst I beamed triumphantly. He left the compartment muttering something about 'the kids of today'. I fell back into the luxurious seat, as the door closed, put my feet back on the seat opposite, admired my bulge and laughed my triumph loud and long.

Not long now and I'd be out of this poverty ridden city for good. No more beatings from my father's thick leather belt. No more violence. How I hate violence. No more having to break school canes so that little kids can be protected from sadistic teachers. No more having to have sex with perverted teachers in the stock room whilst my mates played football. No more making women angry at me on the streets, in order to distract them from beating the hell out of the kids they'd thoughtlessly brought into the world. No more drunken talk of Catholics and Protestants or Irish politics. No more 'working class' snobbery. No more selling my body for peanuts. No more! No more!

Try as I might to hang on to my laughter, it turned to tears which I wiped away with the sleeves of my jacket as rapidly as they fell. 'You're out of it now!' I told myself. 'Forget it!' 'Rent boys don't cry!'

The carriage jolted as the engine was attached. Soon! Not long now. Winding down the window as far as it would go I leant out and looked along the curve of the busy platform at the magnificent engine, throbbing its energy and releasing jets of white hot steam, shsssh! I tried not to look at the people on the platform, now beginning to wave fond farewells to their loved ones, as the engine began to move, shsssh, shsssh, shsssh. All along the length of the train people were leaning out and waving. Smiling faces began to pass by as the train dragged itself forward.

The faces moved along and past my window with increasing speed as my eyes fell upon the warm open face of a woman, old enough to be my mother. To such a face, I could but smile in return. It was as though she was there to wave and smile for those of us without loved ones. I raised both my arms high and waved a farewell to the woman and to the city I both loved and hated. The engine, picking up speed, began its roar of athletic, energetic authority. *No more shit, out of it, no more shit, out of it. Don't cry, why should I? Don't cry, oh not I, oh not I, young rent boys don't cry.*

The steam and smoke licked all around me, as we entered the tunnel at the end of the platform, and brought me to my senses. I was the last remaining person hanging out of the windows. I wiped my face of Liverpool forever and fell tired into my seat.

Leaving Liverpool was easy for nothing held me to it. When a boy leaves the arms of a caring and cared-for lover he instinctively knows that the lover wants him to return to the warm sheets again.

The vampire Liverpool had used me up and was tired of me. It needed fresh blood. Liverpool was a cold hearted lover and wanted the instant and immediate gratification of its own self generated lust. It lusted after the images and fantasies of its own making, and therefore, could never be at ease with itself. Its appetite for fresh faced kids was, and probably still is, insatiable. As a lover, it was a perverted and sadistic nymphomaniac, it used and abused kids; never satisfied, it moved from one fresh kid to the next in search of what the first had actually provided, his innocence! Why should it bother with one kid when it had an endless supply? Why indeed? Why, at fifteen, did I feel so very old?

Leaving my parents was almost as easy. I felt bound to them, a mixture of choking, swaddling clothes and chains. My father's only physical contact with me was through his violent bricklayer's belt. Why did he feel that he could knock either love or sense into me? Why did he never hold me in his arms, just once, and tell me that he loved me? Or that he wanted me to be near him? Was I such a horrible boy? If I was so terrible, then, why did all those other men run their hands through my blond hair, over my smooth skin, between my hairless legs and over my round bottom and tell me that I was so beautiful? Why did I melt into their arms when they said such things to me? Why did I want to please these men so much? Is it really so simple that I hated my father yet wanted his love and found that love in other men? Homosexual men? In pleasing these men was I really attempting to please my father? You see, I also wanted, at various times, to kill him. Indeed, it was only lack of courage and an inner rejection of violence which actually prevented me from doing so. In that private area in my head, where a boy can make himself a king or a cowboy, I planned the murder countless times but could never carry it through or find the optimum moment.

I knew too, that to kill him would release my tormented mother from dominating aggression and yet also cause her to hate me. I think I loved her, but that love was the kind which has to deny all previous pain in order to be actualised. She, my father and my two older brothers, my baby sister and myself, were past masters at make believe. It was a kind of inbred self deluding mechanism which enabled one to fool oneself into believing anything. I recall, for example, my mother beating the hell out of me until I was black and blue, when I was just a kid, and then, perhaps because of my screams or her own realisation of what she was doing, she stopped and told me that everything was alright and that I was a good boy. I believed, wanted to believe and did believe everything she said. It was weird, but I knew that through it all she loved me. With my father I never knew one way or the other. He locked himself in his own private world and kept everybody else out. It must have been a hellhole of a world, or perhaps it was paradise. I'll never know, and I still ache for that knowledge which could give me some insight into what turned my father to the drunken angry man I watched rot in his own compost.

The cold wind blowing through the open window warmed my Catholic guilt. *'Hail Mary, full of grace, the Lord is with thee, blessed art thou amongst women, and blessed is the fruit of thy womb, Jesus.'* Damn those infernal prayers in my head! I closed the window and watched the cold wind, mixed with smoke and steam, seductively lap against the glass, trying to get at me. It licked out its message, *'Holy Mary mother of God, pray for us sinners now, and at the hour of our death, Amen'*. But, I'm safe, it can't get me. I stand up and double check that the window is closed as tight as it possibly can be. It is! I'm safe. I fall back into the seat with the full weight of relief and say out loud, 'Thank God!' Then, realising what I've just said, I dispairingly laugh at my own trapped incongruence.

The sounds and rhythms of the train all around invited me to drift slowly, with my guilt, into a fitful sleep. 'Running away, running away, running away, running away.'

I'd been 'running away' since I was six or seven years old, but only in or around Merseyside itself. This time, however, I had not the slightest intention of returning. Previously, I'd allowed myself to be picked up by the police, and whilst not telling them my name, they'd eventually find out for themselves and return me home. Then, for a short time, the beating would stop. Running away was my way of controlling my father's violence. I knew precisely what I was doing but not one damn adult around me could see through their closed mind's eye. I never tried to help them, it was up to them to figure it out. No one ever did.

When I was nine years old I ran away to Southport, a holiday town just twenty miles north of Liverpool. I headed straight for the fairground and candyfloss, merry-go-rounds, dodgems, ghost trains, halls of mirrors, rifles, coconuts, doughnuts, Noah's ark, the big dipper, and the gypsy woman who read hands, rock with 'Southport' stamped all the way through, hot dogs with onions, and 'hot teas served here'. Sounds of yellows, reds, greens, oranges, and teenage couples. Smells of happiness, jokes, and 'it's only a tanner and its great'.

I'm safe here, but me feet are killing me; I can feel the backs of me shoes through the holes in me socks, and the pants me mam made from me dad's old suit rubbing against me crotch. But, if I put me hands in me pockets I can push them away from me balls. Jesus, that's great. I wonder if they hurt me dad? The funhouse is packed and the laughing man outside is always happy. Wish I had a shilling. All these people and I'm on me own. But I'm glad they're here. What'll I do when they go? They always do. But I won't think about it. It'sopen for ages yet. If I stand just by that stall door I can feel the warm air wrap my whole body in the taste of onions and doughnuts. That's funny, me throat's gone all dry. Can't swallow. I'll sit in one of the seats, or should I? A fat man is going, and he's left half a sandwich. He must be daft. I'll walk past, grab it, quick like, put it in my shirt, and walk out. Got it! People in the way, can't get out.Fatty's seen me. I'll leg it. Can't. 'Well, you'd flippin well finished with it anyway.' Cold air. Thank God. Tastes good. But I'm hungry now. Wish I didn't have to run away. Me mam'll worry and me dad'll get me anyway. Our kid'll have all the bed tonight. Wish I'd brought a coat with me. I didn't want to run away. The lights are going out. Why are they all looking at me like that? I'm nine and can swim, got a certificate. It's cold and I've got a pain in me belly. I wonder which side our kid's sleeping on tonight. If he's on my side I'll kill him. Time to let the police see me. It's been long enough now. He'll be sober now. It'll be okay.

Running away, running away, running away, running away. My sleeping body senses the sounds and rhythms of the train changing: *Hate his feel, screeching wheel, down at heel; He likes my hair, I don't care, get the fare; Out of luck, what the fuck, I can suck! Hissing brakes, big mistakes, even breaks!* I'm shuddered awake as the train comes to a halt at Crewe station. Why do I feel so scared and hungry?

The whole world seems to be at Crewe station. Hundreds of soldiers, sailors and airmen bustle heartily about, singing, shouting. Voices, with unfamiliar accents, call from one side of the never ending platform to another. Men in railway uniform push enormous baskets of mail towards the train. Women in overalls move along the platform selling tea and sandwiches from mobile trolleys. Carriage doors are opened and closed, as more passengers get on than off. All the movement excites me and I forget my fear and hunger for the moment. I catch sight of a family. A mother and father, a girl of about ten years of age and a beautiful boy about a year younger than me. He's dressed in a suit, is wearing a scarf and has his overcoat hung accross his shoulders like a Frenchman. His parents are fussing with luggage, whilst he leans casually on one leg, hand on hip. His eyes wander at sights quite familiar to him. He's a seasoned traveller and no doubt smells of quality soap. His eyes stop at mine and are held there, as he catches me watching him. Time freezes. He blushes and so do I. I venture a smile but his attention is now with his mother, who hands him a piece of expensive hand luggage, pointing to the first class compartments. He looks my way, before moving with his family to that area of the train in which I want to be, smiling. I shiver but manage to smile too.

'Tea? Coffee? Sandwiches?'

A trolley lady, full of music, is before me at the open window, eager for a response in order to sell as much as she can before the train moves out.

'No thanks, it's okay.' I lie, my hunger returning.

'Suit yourself, love.' She sings, moving to the next window.

I want to ask her what time the train is due to arrive at London but she's gone and taken her music with her.

Impulsively, I dash from the train on to the crowded platform and race to the first class section. There he is, third carriage from the front, four carriages from mine. Time stands still, sounds stop and I hear myself, *'Oh sweet and gentle youth, are you all that you seem?'* He raises his beautiful head, his black hair falls across his clear olive face, he lifts his long lashes and winks at me just once. It's all so unreal.

Reality grabs me as the train began to move. I barely make it and find four soldiers in my compartment.

'Only just, kid.' One of them congratulated.

'Flash Gordon.' said another.

They all laughed and one poked me in the ribs. They seemed a nice bunch.

'I was just trying to get a sandwich...' I lied.

'The point is, young scouse, it would appear that you've either scoffed it, dropped it or didn't you actually get your butty?' said the rib poker, mimicking my accent. I didn't get it.

'What do you mean, scouse?'

'You're a scouse, right?'

I looked blankly at him.

'You're from Liverpool aren't you?'

I nodded.

'Then you're a scouse. A scouse is a Liverpudlian.'

'I'm Irish!' I countered, quite insulted. 'A scouse is a pan of stew.'

'The hell you are, you're as English as this damn train and you're a scouse if ever I heard one. We're all Taffs. From north Wales?'

'I'm not, I'm Irish! I should know.'

'Where were you born?' asked one of the others.

'In Liverpool, of course.'

'Then you're a scouse.' They chanted as one voice.

'A scouse?' I tested.

'A scouse.' They laughed.

So I was a scouse and I was English. Weird. It may sound daft, and it does now, but up until that point in my life I considered myself to be completely Irish. No one had ever told me that I was English. I had a whole new identity and that thrilled me enormously.

'Here scouse, get you laughing gear around that,' said the rib poker, as he threw me half a pork pie.

12

His generosity and warm teasing felt good to be near. I thanked him and tried not to eat too fast. A bottle of beer was passed around and I took a swig. Tea would have been better, but nonetheless, it went down well. Cigarettes were produced and openly shared even after I'd told them I had none to share in return. I drank in the all male atmosphere with relish. They told dirty joke after dirty joke, some of which I didn't understand but at which I laughed, so as to be part of them.

'So where you off to then, scouse?' asked rib poker, after the others settled down to snooze.

'London.' I said, with more than a little pride. 'I'm going to London.'

'I know, I mean, I figured that out all by myself. The train is most definitely going to London. Where then?'

His humour pleased me and his perception shook me. He must have been some kind of expert body language reader, or something, for he didn't give me a chance to answer.

'You're on the run, right?'

'Kind of.'

'From the police?'

'From home.'

'Rough, eh?'

'Kind of. I'm just pissed off, you know?'

'Your old man?'

'Yeh.'

'You got any money?'

'No, but I'm okay.'

'How the hell are you going to manage without money?' He asked, very concerned.

'I'll be okay, I can manage.'

'You been to London before, then?'

'It's my first time.'

'I don't see how you're going to manage. You want to get your arse in the army or the merchant navy or something. Good food, good life, know what I mean? Plenty of mates? Loads of scouses!'

'Yeh, but not for me. I've had all the discipline I need.'

'It's not that bad, straight up. Not in the merchant navy anyway.'

'I'll be okay. I'm dying for a piss, I didn't have time at Crewe. I'm bursting.'

'There's bogs at the end of the corridor.' He said, amazed that I didn't know.

13

'Honest? I thought I'd have to wait until the next station.'

'You're joking! You're not! You're dead serious! London's going to chew you up and spit you out. Look, scouse, do yourself a favour and get in the army just as soon as you're old enough. How old are you anyway? You might get into the merchant navy, soonish.'

'Seventeen.' I lied, but my face deliberately telling the truth to my genial inquisitor.

'And I'm Mickey Mouse. What are you? thirteen? fourteen?'

As I left the compartment and swung on the door, I confessed to my new friend that I was fifteen really but I felt older.

'Jail bait!' He laughed, pointing the way. 'Go on before you piss yourself.'

I liked him for he treated me as an equal and hadn't talked down to me. He was nothing like I thought a soldier would be. He was fun to be with. Perhaps the army was full of guys like him. Or the merchant navy. See the world? Adventure? Worth thinking about.

Having made full use of the bogs I began to make my way tentatively towards the first class section, four carriages away, three from the front. My heart raced and thumped out the truth, I was infatuated with a beautiful boy who was a total stranger. It wasn't love, for that requires a knowledge of the other person, which I didn't have. What was it about him which had so fixated me? Why did I feel this way? What might his name be? I guessed at 'Simon'. Where was he headed? Had he really seen me, and winked? Was I making a fool of myself? Would he laugh in my face?

I entered his carriage and walked slowly along the corridor looking into each compartment. This was crazy. I must be out of my mind. What on earth could a penniless street kid have in common with *Simon*? Absolutely nothing! About to turn and head back to my own carriage, I saw him, and carried on walking, trying to catch my breath. So beautiful, so like Mike, my best friend. The friend I hadn't even told that I was leaving. Couldn't tell him, you see? Not that I was going to London forever. I vowed to telephone him from London, when I got settled. Had he seen me, Simon? I waited at the end of the corridor for what seemed like a reasonable time and then headed back along the way I'd come. There was no mistaking it this time, for our eyes met, nervously. Once again, I stopped at the recess at the end of the carriage, out of breath and heart racing. I heard a compartment door slide open and soft footsteps coming my way. I closed my eyes, and opened them to see him standing not twelve inches from me. Oh dear God, what now?

'I am Alexander, what do they call you?'

'Scouse.'

'Scouse?'

'I'm from Liverpool. You?'

'We travel considerably. My Father is with the Army.'

I couldn't for the life of me think of anything else to say. I just looked at his magnificent olive skinned beauty. He moved closer. His fragrant aura enveloping our dual vulnerability.

'I saw you, from the platform, at Crewe.' He whispered.

'Yes?'

'You were looking at me?'

'Yes, yes I was.' His face was inches away. His hazel eyes searched mine, and mine his.

'You are very good looking.' He ventured.

I blushed.

'Thanks, I mean, so are you, I mean, I'd like…'

'Yes?'

'You know, to be with you.'

'And I would like to be with you also.'

A compartment door slid open and then closed. Someone was coming. The train went across an intersection, as though answering my prayers, for we were thrown together. Arms went around waists, stomachs touched, legs went between legs, our lips met in the faintest most tentative kiss and we both smiled, relieved. He tasted heavenly and looked radiantly content.

. The footsteps were getting nearer. Sensing that our magical twinkling moment was about to end, he whispered his London telephone number into my ear. He had to repeat it three times for his breath on my cheeks intensified my already heightened sensations, electrified my skin and caused my head to swim. Then, turning quickly, he headed back to his compartment just as a woman came into view. The telephone number circled in my head, as I made my way back giddily along the train towards my own class, and I knew that as long as I lived, I'd never be able to forget it.

The good natured soldiers were fast asleep in my compartment so I left it to them and decided, alternatively, to explore the remainder of the train.

Why is it that boys like to lean out of the windows of moving trains? Well, that's what I did instead of looking into carriage after

15

carriage, which I figured would be much the same as each other anyway. I went to the end of the corridor and opened the window all the way down, and popped my head and shoulders out into the fast moving air. It was wonderful.

I didn't see the fields racing by, nor hear the rattle of the train on the tracks, nor smell the engine, nor taste the smoke. I could see Alexander in his bedroom, could feel his warm eager flesh close to mine as we slipped naked beneath the crisp sheets, could taste his tender full lips and hear his whispering voice saying, 'I want to be with you'. I was impervious to all else until a hand touched my shoulder. Turning, I saw a well dressed man of about thirty.

'Do you by any chance have a light?' He said, offering me a cigarette.

I didn't, but I did have an erection, which gained his attention. Tell tale signs indicated his approval and interest. I'd seen all the signs before; furtive glances to check the coast was clear, prolonged eye contact, an uneasy caution, a dropping of the normal verbal communication level, a closing down of one's physical borders, the touching of his own aroused sex and the silent questions.

'How far are you going?' He asked, still unsure of his ground.

'How far do you want me to go?' I replied, putting him at his ease.

More confident now, he moved closer, put the cigarettes away and touched the bulge in my trousers. Pearls of sweat on his forehead betraying his desire.

'Come in here.' He urged, holding the toilet door ajar, waiting for me to follow.

'Perhaps.' I said, and waited to see his next move.

'I'll pay you!' He said, almost apologetically.

'How much?'

This was no time to beat about the bush. I had a reasonably good looking punter before me with money to spare, and I was flat broke. He drew out his wallet and I put my hand out, and kept it there until the required amount was placed in the palm of my hand.

Inside the toilet cubicle, with the door firmly closed, he undid my trousers at the top, slipped the zip down and let the trousers hang loose whilst he unfastened my shirt, exposing my naked torso.

'You're so very lovely.' He praised. Oh, how I liked his praise. I

16

responded by becoming more fully erect. Slowly he worked his hands and lips downwards, until he was on his knees before me. There, taking my trousers and underpants down as far as my ankles. His mouth closed over my erect cock and he licked and sucked it like an expert, whilst his hands played over my smooth belly and chest. I closed my eyes and let my thoughts return to Alexander.

Like most punters, the moment he came his load, he got away from the object of his desire just as quickly as he could. I stayed in the toilet, stripped completely naked and made an attempt at a soul cleansing stand up bath; for, like most Catholic rent boys, I always felt as guilty as hell afterwards. But time is a great healer, both of guilt and pain.

What would Alexander think of me if he knew that the blond haired boy he'd kissed on a train was no more than a wretched rent boy? Surely, I reasoned, he wouldn't want anything to do with me ever again, I mean, who would? How to reconcile what I was with how I wanted to be, alongside Alexander. I tried not to think about it.

Relief came only when the train finally pulled into London's Euston station. People from the second class carriages, with heavy bags, were looking for porters but they were already unloading the expensive luggage at the first class section on to trolleys. They were not like me. That is, they were one class, serving another. I wanted to be that other, to wear expensive clothes like Alexander and have porters rush to carry my bags, as the porters now carried his family's. I determined, there and then, to live and travel first class just as soon as I possibly could. I couldn't tell if he turned to wave or not for the crowds pushed their way through and I just stopped still and allowed them to do so. I heard a voice calling,

'Scouse! Eh, scouse!'

It was rib poker. He dashed passed and pushed an envelope into my hands. 'Look after yourself, jail-bait,' he called as he rushed to catch up with his friends. I waved but soon lost sight of him in the crowd, then he was gone. The envelope contained a one pound note and a brief letter, with his address:

Dear Scouse,

Or, should I call you jail-bait? You know what I'm getting at

17

don't you? Ha! Ha! Take it easy around the Dilly. Seriously though I'd love to run my fingers through your hair. You're a nice kid and I'm worried that you're in for a rough time, so I hope you'll accept the enclosed. I know it's not much but I've just been on leave. I like you, scouse, and if you ever get lonely then drop me a line, I'd really like to see you again. I get lonely for someone like you.

Yours ever, Taff (Joseph)

I read and re-read the letter, tears unashamedly falling on to the page of Joseph's notebook. He knew! How could he know? He had seen right through me! He wanted to be near me! He knows! I'm heading for that place called 'The Dilly' and he knows why, and he still wants to be near me!

After what seemed no time at all I was the only person left on the platform. I looked around, it was bigger than Liverpool. Fear gripped me so I took a hold of myself, recalled that rent boys don't cry and headed for the exit.

I'd arrived. I was in London. There was no turning back now.

Joker's Wild

I sucked in the glorious evening anonymity of rush hour in the bustling concourse of Euston station and let out a whistle of absolute schoolboy delight. I'd never seen so many people, not all in one place before. If this was London, I already loved it, for, not one person paid me the slightest notice and that's just the way I wanted it to be. I needed merely to melt into the place and become part of it. Why had Joseph feared that London would chew me up and spit me out? No way! He obviously didn't know just how streetwise I was. I mean, I'd arrived in London with more than I'd set out with, and I had his address, and, most valuable of all, I had met Alexander. London? A piece of cake!

I bought a packet of cigarettes, a box of matches, a pen and a pocket sized notebook from a kiosk. In the back of the notebook I wrote Alexander's name and telephone number, not because I might forget them, there was not a chance of that. I just wanted to see his name in writing. Below that, I copied Joseph's name and address, because there was every chance I'd forget them. Why are some things easier to remember than others? Turning to the front page of the notebook I wrote in my best handwriting:

Alexander

Alexander, I believe I
Love you;
Even though I am a
Xen in your world.
Any place you are, I
Need to be, however
Dichotomously.
Ever yours,
Richie.

That one page contained two very special secrets; my love of a dark-haired boy and my love of the sounds and shapes of words. Although I wasn't the most outward going or gregarious person in the world, I did have an inner facility to create pictures in my mind. This facility was born out of necessity, as a way of getting away from the harsh realities of my father and his drunken violence; I would travel inwards to a world more beautiful. A world of colour and enchanting words. A world where I could use words in any way I wanted to. As I would find out later, these words were considered, by others, to be poetry. Yet, I'd always hated 'poetry' and usually when I spoke to other people I was almost monosyllabic. Why should that be? I'm sorry, there I go again with my 'why' questions. I can't help it. You know what I mean? Perhaps you can work things out better for yourself, than I could then.

I closed the notebook and placed it carefully in my inside coat pocket, next to my heart. I was too thrilled to think straight but I did know that I didn't want to get on another train so soon, even if they did call it a 'tube' and even if it did only take a few minutes to get to the West End. I needed to walk, to feel the air, to get into wider space. So, having discovered the general directions to Soho, from a prissy woman in a fur coat, I set off in search of what it had to offer. I would telephone Alexander tomorrow.

There was no mistaking Soho. All life was there, an international blend of laughter, colour and strange behaviour. I was instantly addicted to the place. Time and order had no meaning here, it was heaven sent adolescent anarchy. Flashing lights and strip joints; restaurants and card sharks; provocative girls and theatres; every language and every fantasy; wealth and money; coffee bars and jukeboxes; and still more money! I was in paradise!

Cold, hunger and tiredness took me into a coffee bar called the Two 'I's' in Old Compton Street, where I drank frothy coffee for the first time and where I made my first mistake. That is, I paid for myself! Time would teach me not to do that very often. As I drank the strange and enjoyable mixture I reminded myself that months before I'd written, *'Watch for punters, learn the score, money first, then his pleasure, make the punter want you more'*. I let myself off the hook, however, telling myself that it was my first night, and besides money was all around, just waiting to be picked up. Convinced of this, I ordered a hamburger and another frothy coffee and sat back to listen to a song, which had been released just a couple of months before, on the jukebox. It was the new rock 'n' roll idol, Cliff Richard with The Drifters singing 'Move it'. Whilst listening to the record, I overheard the folks on the next table excitedly telling each other that Cliff Richard started by singing in this very coffee bar, as had Tommy Steele. I really was in paradise. Cliff Richard was the first British 'pop idol' to attract me, and I realised that it was more than likely that he would have sat as close to the jukebox as I now sat. Perhaps, in the same seat. Paradise, indeed. Why is it, do you suppose, that so many adults fail to understand a boy's adulation of his favourite pop idol?

Reluctantly, I left the Two 'I's and followed my nose through streets which I would come to know well, down Old Compton Street, into Brewer Street; turn left into the fabulously narrow and packed Great Windmill Street, then, right onto Shaftesbury Avenue. There, before me was the object of my journey, Piccadilly Circus!

Having walked around it at least a dozen times, taking in its magic, I settled myself against the railings, under the arches of Barclays Bank, by the number one tube exit and lit a cigarette. Without realizing, I'd landed, somehow instinctively, on the place known to all as 'The Meat Rack'.

It was a natural choice. The arches of the building above gave protection from the November cold and rain, whilst the warm air, rising from the underground railway, gave one a marked advantage over the folks on the other side of the road. Why 'The Meat Rack?' Because boys hung around the railings waiting for punters, like marketable produce in a butcher's shop. Body posture and eye contact being the 'for sale' signs.

There was no shortage of boys out tonight. I stood between a cute faced kid of about sixteen and boy in a motorcycle jacket, who I guessed to be about eighteen. They seemed to know each other. Too many for business? I initially thought so but no sooner had I lit my cigarette than the punters took notice, my sign was up. Men moved purposely from boy to boy sounding out their sexual preferences and price. I turned down three offers because they were too kinky.˙ One wanted me to spank him, another wanted me to dress as a girl and the third wanted to drink my piss. I wasn't shocked, I'd had such offers back home. It just wasn't my scene. The cute friendly faced kid went off happily with the piss drinker, throwing me a wink as he went. Minutes later the boy in the motorcycle jacket went off with the guy who wanted to be spanked. I waited.

Suddenly, the Rack emptied of boys and punters alike. I was completely baffled. I'd made my second, and what could have been a very costly mistake. That is, I stayed. The sight of the blue uniform enabled me to put two and two together quite rapidly, however, and I made tracks. When the blue-bottle was out of sight, the Rack resumed its normal activity once again. I knew I'd been lucky and thoughts of being dragged back to Liverpool made it unlikely for me not to spot a policeman ever again. I took up my place and waited, but I must have been sending out all the wrong signals for punters stepped cautiously around me. Experience would soon instruct me that a punter can smell a nervous and frightened kid a mile away. The agitated nervous signals the kid sends out are like signs to prison, easily avoided. Why risk a kid unsure of himself when the Rack is full of willing boys?

By the time I'd regained my composure the cute faced kid was back on the Rack, smiling and chatting to the other boys. It was clear that he was was very popular and was taking an interest in me, so I smiled. He quickly saw the invitation and came directly up to me, as though he'd known me all my life;

'Watcha! You're new right? Not seen you around before.

How's business? There's a nip in the air, 'aint there? Do you know what Baden-Powell said when he started up the Boy Scouts? He said, and I've got to talk like Churchill to get this, he said, "...I have seen thousands of boys and young men, narrow chested, hunched up, miserable specimens, smoking endless cigarettes..."'

I laughed at his marvellous performance. He went on,

'He should've come round here, right? Can you imagine it? We'd all have bleedin' funny hats on an' uniforms, an' short trousers, bleedin' punters would go crazy for it. You don't say much, do yer? What's yer handle? What do we call yer? Can't live without a bit of a laugh, right? Do you like Skiffle? I think Lonnie Donegan is fantastic. Come on, say something.'

I was still laughing. I offered him a cigarette and we lit up.

'My name is Richie, what's yours?' I asked, eager to know this cute kid.

'Blimey, you *are* new 'aint yer?' He scolded.

'What do you mean?'

'No names, no pack drill, know what I mean? They call me *Joker.*'

'Sure, I'm Scouse.'

'See yer round scouse, that punter over there, the one with the raincoat over his arm, he's taken a shine to you, say no more, don't do anything I wouldn't do, see yer later, okay?'

'Okay,' I agreed.

The punter was a shy American businessman, lonely for the company of a boy. He was staying at the Regent's Palace hotel just across the street and he smelt of money.

'I have yet to eat. Are you hungry?' He tested.

'Growing boys are always hungry, you should know that.'

We ate a magnificent meal at the Chinese restaurant which overlooks The Meat Rack. He skillfully sidestepped any talk of himself, other than to say he was a businessman, and brought the conversation around to me. He seemed keen to know all about my life. Why should that be? I lied about everything. I told him that my name was Mark Crosbie, that I knew London well, that I was staying with friends of the family near by, that I went to public school in southern Ireland and that I'd spent my allowance all too quickly. He asked if I would object to him helping me out with a small gift. I blushed, out of guilt that he was falling for all the bull, but which he took as embarrassment. He apologised for offending me and assured me that he meant no harm. I thanked him for his generous offer and told him that under the circumstances I'd accept, but only if he'd have coffee with me at his hotel. His face lit up and he placed the money for the bill on a side plate and pushed a further twenty pounds across the table towards me. I folded this with care and then slipped it in between the pages of my notebook, inside my jacket pocket. We understood each other perfectly.

On the street, as we neared his hotel, he suggested that he go in first, to 'order coffee', and for me to follow in ten minutes. We could then enjoy it in the privacy of his room. I agreed, saying that I had to buy some cigarettes anyway. I left him on the corner and never saw him again. As I watched him going into the hotel I rejoined Joker.

'Watcha scouse, how'd it go? He was a Yank, wasn't he? You know what Henry Miller says about Yanks don't yer? He says, "...The American ideal is youth – handsome, empty youth..." But is he right, I mean, who's empty? The Youth or the Yank? Is the Yank's wallet lighter or not? And, is the handsome youth full? Which is it? You may speak.'

'I don't know where you get it all from.' I said, spellbound by his seductive charm.

'Tis but a sign of a good education. So? Which is it?'

'I got a meal and twenty quid!'

'Not bad, not bad at all. But one must learn whether to collect the stuff or spend it. I've got a tenner, what do yer say we go to the pictures? Then, a bleedin' feast of hamburgers, an' then you can doss down at the flat afterwards. Speak, northern mortal, speak.'

'Terrific.' I enthused, eager to spend as much time with Joker as possible. 'You've got your own flat?'

'No, I share with a bunch of others in Kangaroo Valley, Don't worry, it's sound.'

'Kangaroo Valley?'

'Forget it, you'll soon know yer way around.'

At the cinema I produced my notebook and took the money from it. Joker's keen eyes spotted my piece on Alexander, as my eyes too were held by it.

'Did you write that?'

'Yes, today.' I said, slightly peeved that he was looking, but pleased at his interest.

'Can I read it?'

He sounded sincere and I'd warmed to him. I gambled and let him see it.

'That's sound. Real sound.'

'Keep it to yourself, please, Joker?'

'Leave it out, what do yer take me for? I'm telling yer, it's sound, 'aint I? Is he a scouse too?'

'No, he lives in London. I'll tell you all about him one day, okay.'

'Sound. Yeh.'

Joker let me pay for the tickets and I let him know that I was treating him, this time, after all.

'You're the one who spotted the punter.'

The changed expression on Joker's face told me to put my brain in gear. It then dawned on me that Joker had set me up with the punter and could just as easily have had him himself.

'You're something else. You set me up, right?'

Joker was pleased that I'd seen his generosity at last, and shrugged his shoulders, as if to say, 'So what?'

'Thank you, Joker.'

'Don't get all serious on me, it was nothing, forget it, enjoy yourself, okay?'

'Okay, but I pay for everything, right.' I insisted.

'Now, you're getting the picture.' He laughed, letting me.

'You crafty son of a bitch.'

'Consider it a lesson from a master, me old mate. You'll learn, yet. Put it down to experience!'

And that's just what I did. I liked Joker, who could fail not to? His cute open face; his warm and friendly laugh; his knowledge of the street; his constant quotes – from god knows where; his caring; his roguishness; his ability to survive. I admired him greatly, and told him so, as we took our seats to watch a Hammer horror film.

'You're okay, yourself.' Was all he'd say, and he never spoke another word until the film was over. After hamburgers and bottles of Coke we took a taxi to Warwick Road in Earl's Court. In the cab, I asked Joker how it was that he was always so cheerful. He paused, looked at me and then quite seriously he said,

'That poem, you know, the one you wrote about Alex something or other...'

'Alexander.' I corrected.

'Yea, that's it. Anyway, you love him, right?'

24

'I think so. I'm not sure.'

'Take my word for it, you do! At least, somewhere inside you, you do. Anyway, he's not here with you, is he? I mean, something keeps you apart? Well, it's like that with me.'

'I'm not sure I follow you.'

'It's simple, look, I love happiness, but where the friggin' hell am I going to find it on these streets? Nowhere, that's where! So, I make my own, it's simple.'

He pulled a small book from his pocket and showed it to me. It was a book of quotations.

'Keep this to yourself, right? See this, this is my passport out of here. I learn one of these a day and one day I'll go to college or something and kiss goodbye to all this.'

'I follow you, but how do you make happiness?'

'The same way you make mistakes, by being yourself. Look, no one gives a toss about the likes of you and me. They think we're toe rags, right? So, they expect us to be like toe rags all of the time. Well, I mess up their biased expectations, don't I? I'm never like the way they expect and I'm dead chuffed about that. It's the same with you, 'aint it? I mean, a rent boy who writes poetry, see what I mean?

'Yes, I think I do. There's more to you than meets the eye. You're something else Joker, I'm real glad to know you.' I said, sincerely, offering him my hand.

'Understandable, perfectly understandable.' He teased, shaking my hand warmly and returning to his former self.

Joker confidently instructed the taxi driver to stop the cab on the corner, by a pub called 'The Lord Ranelagh,' waited for me to pay, which I dutifully did.

'You'll need a couple of things, to pave the way, kind of thing, with the others.' He instructed, leading me like a pupil to the corner shop.

'What kind of things? Do all the shops stay open this late?'

'It's not that late, I guess they do, never thought about it. Keep it simple, coffee, tea, biscuits, milk, that kind of thing. Here, do you shave?'

I didn't, but blushed at the memory of trying to do so once, about six months previously. Having found nothing to shave on my face, I'd shaved off my pubic hair and luxuriated in the pre-pubescent feel of my body.

'No, I don't shave, not yet.'

25

'Me neither, thank Christ. Just get some soap then. You can use my towel. Oh, an' get some sweets for Angel.'

'Angel?'

'You'll see, he's okay, but watch him, he can be a right son of a bitch when he wants.'

The shopping complete we headed for a house on Warwick Road, near to Earl's Court Square. Joker led the way down the basement steps, fished around under some plant pots and brought out a key, which he used to open the door.

'Here, stick that back will yer.' He said, handing me the key. 'It's always there, so you'll know yer way in from now on, okay?'

I put the key back but was tempted to turn on my heels for I felt anxious about what I was getting myself into. Why should this cute faced kid take an interest in me? Perhaps, I was being set up to be rolled?' Joker kicked the door closed and, seeing my face, said,

'Come on, relax, it's sound.'

'Then why the hell am I shaking?'

Joker had no time to answer. Out of the kitchen came the prettiest boy I'd ever seen, dressed in a white bathrobe and look-ing exactly like a twelve year old choirboy, a piece of toast in his hands. Looking at me but speaking to Joker, he asked,'

'Who's he?'

'This, Angel, is the *Poet*. He's one of us an' he's staying.'

I looked at Joker in blank amazement. The 'Poet?' Was this to be my new name? Surely, he wasn't going to speak about Alexander?

Angel's eyes were now on the carrier bag.

'Sure, there's space. Hello Poet, been shopping?'

'Yes, just some essentials. I thought, well Joker thought, that perhaps, that you might like these?' I said, nervously handing Angel the sweets.

Angel was aptly named. He was strikingly beautiful, angelic, with soft white skin. He held the packet of sweets to his chest, as a child would hold a precious toy. Joker's warning about this gentle child must have been a total lie. Why would he lie? Perhaps, they were lovers? Perhaps, this was Joker's way of saying, 'hands off'. Angel thanked me and silently followed Joker and I into the kitchen, where I unloaded the other bits of shopping onto the crowded work surface.

Whilst Joker made a pot of tea, Angel asked me how old I was.

I told him fifteen, which delighted him for some reason. He wanted to know precisely when I'd turned fifteen and danced with joy around the kitchen when I told him last month, October 28th. Joker explained as Angel went dancing through the flat. It transpired that the Joker was sixteen, that Angel was fifteen, and until my arrival had been the youngest in the flat. As things turned out Angel was two months older than me.

Carrying mugs of tea, I followed Joker through the flat, as he explained things to me and introduced me to the others.

The flat, it seemed, belonged to Actor's sugar-daddy. Actor was a kind of vague soul, lost in his own world of Hollywood and dreams of becoming famous. He was nineteen, good looking and could do what he liked with the flat, and himself, just so long as he didn't have 'it' off with anyone else. He chose to surround himself with those he felt familiar with and superior to, rent boys. His stage career, seemingly, was held back only by his voice and he worked hard to try to get rid of his Birmingham accent, which amounted to him putting the word 'actually' at the beginning, sometimes in the middle and always at the end, of every sentence. His first words to me were,

'Actually, you may stay, it's £1 a week, actually, paid on Fridays, in cash, there's a spare bed in Joker's room, actually.'

I was to share a room with Joker, Angel and seventeen year old Magpie. Magpie, apparently, was not expected back for 'quite some time' because he'd stolen anything and everything which hadn't been nailed down, though not from the flat; he was currently doing time.

The other room was shared by Biker and sometimes his girl, Flyer and Banker. I recognised Biker as the boy from The Meat Rack, the one with the leather coat, who went of with the guy who wanted spanking. He pulsed aggression and 'fuck' proved to be his favourite word.

'Fucking good to see a friendly fucking face around here,' was his welcome to me.

He scared me but I, nonetheless, sensed that he wasn't such a bad person. He was eighteen, the same as Flyer, who was out trying to score a fix. Flyer, it seemed was into just about any drug he could lay his hands on, and would do anything he had to in order to get high, to fly. Banker, the oldest in the flat, at twenty, kept himself to himself and struck me as being kind of weird. He saved every penny he could get, for what? That it seems was his secret.

Actor had his own room, into which no other person was ever invited whilst he was in the flat. When he went out, the room had two huge padlocks fitted, which were securely tightened; and, which, according to Joker, were the biggest talked about living problem in an otherwise sound arrangement. Biker, it seems, had more than once, threatened to 'smash the fucking door down' to see what the big mystery was.

The rules of the flat were simple, there weren't any! Except for one, no punters! Otherwise, it was an open house. Do as you like. Sleep as long as you wanted, when you wanted. If you could afford it, you were expected to buy food.

None of the flat sharers questioned my new found name. To them I was the Poet. This embarrassed and amused me. Based on one piece of writing, I'd become a poet. The instant and unquestioning recognition was, however, a boost to my confidence. Perhaps Joker was right, perhaps one could create one's own world, simply by being oneself. The trick was to make constant and consistent choices to be whatever it was one wanted. Joker, more than anything, wanted to be happy. Whilst I wanted to runaway from violent rejection. Was there a difference?

Back in the kitchen, and more relaxed that the unknown wasn't so terrible after all, I listened, along with hovering Angel, to Joker's latest impromptu performance of Churchill, with eager ears:

'You should write about rent boys, Poet. For, as Henry Miller once said, "...The poem is the dream made flesh, in a two-fold sense as a work of art, and as life which is a work of art..." And we are dreams made flesh. We are the dreams of tired and lonely men, mostly married, who seek to recapture, or discover for the first time, the beauty of being a boy. We do a great public service when we melt our lives into their dreams. The rent boy's life is a multicoloured work of art, a tapestry, but alas, there are many weavers and only one boy, one piece of fine sculptured cloth. The rent boy is a living poem and the poet must find the words hidden within him. You think I jest?'

'I jest think you're bonkers,' laughed Angel.

I shared Angel's laughter, but secretly wished to learn more from Joker. I applauded his performance and told him that he was a real artist, that he should go on the stage.

'I'm already on it!' He laughed, bowing to the applause. 'Come on, let me show yer where you're kipping.'

The 'beds' were four mattresses, one in each corner of the room, each with a couple of sheets and blankets simply arranged on top. As we prepared for bed, and no doubt infected by Joker's humour, Angel told me that he knew some poetry, and proceeded to recite:

> 'She stood on the bridge at moonlight,
> Her lips were all aquiver.
> She gave a cough,
> Her leg fell off
> And floated down the river.'

We groaned and hissed our way between the sheets of our separate beds and Joker put the light out. Ten minutes or so later, Joker whispered,

'Poet, you okay?'

'Sound, Joker, thanks.'

Sleep came easily after that, despite the sound of Radio Luxembourg coming from the next room. Bad dreams, however, came just as easily, and it wasn't long before my mind was full of violent confrontations. I was fighting with my drunken father and was shouting at him to leave my mother alone. He was cursing, throwing plates of food into the back of the fire, screaming at my mother that she couldn't cook as well as his mother. Just as he's about to hit her I pick up a knife and throw myself between them. The knife, about to enter his chest for the second time, is dripping blood. I sit bolt upright in my bed, wide awake, sweating profusely, heart racing, eyes full of tears, and me, terrified of my own violent potential. How many times must I have this dream? Why do I cry so? In the shadows, I heard Joker snoring and saw, coming towards my bed, Angel, as naked as the day he was born.

'You need some company,' he whispered. Was he asking, or telling me? Whichever, he wasn't waiting for an answer, he climbed in beside me. My very soul was crying out to be healed of violent dreams; my body longed to be held. I opened my arms to his and kissed his voluptuous full lips as we fell inevitably back into the pillow. My tears fell on his face. His response was instant.

Soft coiling limbs surrounded mine in gentle healing movements. His hands explored and stroked my tear stained face. He comforted me with his own need to be loved. His erect boyhood pressed against the hollow in my belly. He tugged at my underpants, and together we managed to get them down, without our lips parting. Kicking them loose, I became free to allow his smooth hairless boy flesh to move mutually over and against my own naked consent. Our erections danced a sliding, slipping dance. Unaided, we reacted as we should, with spontaneous electrified tactile combustion. There could be only one conclusion. With words, superfluously transcended, the senses came alive.

I touch, hear, smell, taste and see the boy in my arms. What will follow, must follow. There's no order or plan to it. It is what it is. Nothing can be better, surely? He licks my chest, my belly, my thighs and then the full length of my cock. He opens his mouth, and takes me in. Oh my God, I'm ready to explode, but then, perfectly scripted, he moves his attention to the cheeks of my bottom, his body asking mine to turn. He's licking, gently biting. Never have I felt a tongue do that. Moving, so that his body covers mine, I feel his erection slide between my legs. He first senses my delight and then, using nature's lubricant, he enters the mystery within me. I can not hold back, I have to let go. I must erupt. I am erupting. With the knowledge of rhythm, he pulses his shared harmonic melody into our one joint reconciled, inestimable, climax. We gasp for air, not wanting to move. We stay like that, unspeaking, content. With him still inside me, my own belly wonderfully covered, we pant, still in rhythm, for breath; he kisses my neck and we sleep, as one.

In the morning we are two again. Very close, still wrapped in each other's arms, but two. The oneness, a dream, a memory. I wake and look at Angel's face and I want to cry again. Can there be any more beautiful sight than a boy sleeping, so contentedly? I know, deep in my soul, that it can't last, it never does. It can't. As Joker so wisely reflected, our lives, the lives of rent boys, are but a tapestry, woven by many weavers, and we are in their hands. But, what was it he also said? Something, yes something about defying their expectations? My head wants none of it. I can't make head nor tail of it. I want only to be loved, and to love in return.

I hold my breath and begin to count. If I can count to a hundred before taking a breath, if only I can hold my breath long enough, then perhaps, I might slip into that dream sleep where Angel and I were one, reconciled. I make it to seventy-three, and my gasp for air wakens Angel. He rubs his chest, then the sleep from his eyes. When he takes his hands away his face has changed. The new day challenges him to survive. His eyes narrow. His thoughts are elsewhere, and he's not far behind. I say,

'Good morning.'

He looks around, reading the daylight as precisely as only a street-boy can do and says,

'What's the time? Shit!'

'I don't know, I don't have a watch.' I apologise.

'Joker! Joker, what time is it?' He screams, as he jumps from my bed, letting the cold air rush between the sheets in a gust.

'Time? Every bloody day, every day for years, you ask me the same damn question. Get a watch, can't you!'

Angel is pulling his clothes on and becoming more and more agitated.

'Come on Joker, don't piss about, please.' He pleads.

Time? You're obsessed. You're either too early or too late for everything you do. You're never there! You're never on time. It's half eleven.' He concedes, and snuggles back down.

'That's a flippin' untruth, and some people know it, right Poet?' He answers, looking directly at me. 'Sometimes I'm right on time!'

I blush at the eye contact between all three and watch him dash from the room, in triumph.

'Don't worry about it Poet. He always kisses and tells. He can't help it, he just has to tell people. God alone knows why. He's a bit like that boy Holden, in Salinger's *Catcher In The Rye*. You know, he promises not to then does it. He says, "...I keep making up these sex rules for myself and then I break them right away..." Well, Angel always intends not telling, and always does, without fail. Besides, I heard you at it, you noisy pair of sods.'

I make a mental note of the book Joker's just mentioned and ask him where the nearest library is, so that I can borrow it.

'Biker's got a copy, somewhere around the place. You can look for it when you put the kettle on.'

'Very subtle.' I acknowledge, and drag myself from the warm blankets into my cold clothes; and into an even colder kitchen. What a mess. Why is it that teenage boys never wash up after

31

themselves, ever? Waiting for the kettle to boil, I look into the other room. It's in darkness, figures move in fitful sleep. The door to Actor's room is closed and padlocked. He must have left early. Angel dashes from the bathroom, punches my shoulder, winks and is out of the flat, all in a matter of hperactive seconds.

Joker sits up for his tea and pulls a blanket around his shoulders. I return to my bed and do the same. I risk a direct question,

'You know what you were saying, to Angel, about the time? You said he'd been asking you the same question for years? I know it's none of my business, but how long have you known each other?'

Joker, far from being offended at my probing question, put me at my ease;

'We aren't lovers, or anything like that, though, as friends, we have sex, but it doesn't feel right. We're like brothers, see?'

Their brotherhood, he went on to explain, had grown through their meeting in a children's home. From which they were both on the run. I sat silently and listened, transfixed. Joker was an only child but had never known his real father. His mother married again when he was about ten years old. His new 'father' had taken a special interest in him from the start, lavishing time and effort on him. He was a really nice person to have around. He took Joker to the cinema, swimming, everywhere. After a short while Joker had become unashamedly dependent on the attention. Increasingly, however, the attention became sexual. That is, his father would bathe him and linger, with soapy hands, around Joker's genitals. Joker felt no sense of guilt or shame for what happened, since he knew that his father 'loved' him dearly. He told him so many times. By the time he was twelve, Joker was secretly sleeping with his father, when his mother was out, and the relationship had become much more sexual. It was on one of those fully sexual occasions that they'd been discovered, by his mother. The police were called and Joker was taken into 'care' and sent, with all the guilt he could carry, to a kids home. His father was sent to prison and his mother blamed him for breaking up the marriage, which ended in divorce.

At the kids home he was befriended by another new arrival, Angel, who'd been sent there after setting fire to his school having failed to blackmail a teacher. The blackmail had never come out and Angel was sent to see a psychiatrist, who thought he was

32

dangerous. Every week after that, he had to see the trick-cyclist, who was assigned to the kids home. It was a crazy situation. The teacher had been touching Angel up for years and Angel had tried to regain his own sense of power and control, in the only way he knew how; he asked for money. The teacher, with access to hundreds of other kids, had refused and, from then on, shut Angel out. That's when Angel broke into the school and torched his classroom, and the fire got out of control. Angel was arrested, watching the blaze. No one ever asked him why he did it, they simply assumed that he was an emotionally disturbed kid who'd become a danger to society.

Angel learnt his lesson quickly, get the money first in future. He learnt, too, that his seductive pretty face was his greatest asset and soon he had one of the care workers wrapped around his little finger. Money first, then his pleasure. Angel was never short of money, smokes or sweets, which he shared only with Joker. He also came to share the care worker, who became putty in their hands. When the other kids began to put two and two together Joker and Angel went 'on the run'. They'd been undiscovered in London for nearly a year.

'So, Poet, when I saw you on the Dilly yesterday, I spotted a fellow traveller, right?'

'Kind of, I'm on the run but not from a kids home. Though, I seem to have spent my life running away. I always used to dream about being sent to a kids home because I hated my own so much. I used to make things up in my head, you know, stories, fantastic ideas. I could escape in there and live in the story. I even imagined that my parents weren't my real parents and one day my real parents would come and rescue me. Daft eh?'

Joker's face remained serious. I went on to tell him about my drunken father, whose answer to everything was violence, and of my eldest brother who took my adoration of him and twisted it into sexual exploitation. I explained how I'd discovered the rent scene in a public toilet, in a park, when a man offered me money to look at my cock. I told him about being raised as a Catholic and of how guilty I felt every time I had sex with a man. I told him too, of how I'd go with men who were gentle and loving, for free, in the hope that some of the gentleness and love would rub off on me. I confessed to being a good fighter at school simply because one had to be and of how scared I was of just how violent I sometimes felt inside. I owned up that my love of words, their sounds and meanings, had emerged largely out of those stories in my head and from the cinema. I'd read very little 'real' poetry.

We filled in the details of each other's stories and answered each other's questions, unguardedly. As we did so, a special bond was cemented between us.

'There is just one thing, Joker, you warned me that Angel could be evil. What did you mean?'

'It's really simple. You know you were saying about how violent yer old man gets when he's bevied? And, how scared you get with the violence yer feel inside? Well, it's like that with Angel. You've tasted violence, right? You know what it's like. Well, he's tasted evil and knows what that's like. That teacher was no bleeding saint, you know. A kid, you should know this, is like an empty jug and life's experiences fill him up with whatever comes. If good gets in, fine. But, when evil gets in it, well, it just festers and stays around, doesn't it? Just like violence, yeh? The problem is though, that kids can't easily tell the difference between good and evil, they just accept things as they are, right?

'Do you read the papers? You should. There's a black geezer, in America, who understands things so clearly. He's one of them civil rights fellas you know? Anyway, his name is Martin Luther King and he's shit hot. He's always on about freedom and things like that but he stands no chance. Well, as much chance as we stand. Anyway, he's just said, in the papers, he said, "...He who passively accepts evil is as much involved in it as he who helps to perpetrate it..." So, if we live in shit, and we know we live in shit, and then put up with it, we add to it, see what I mean? We have to be different to what the bastards expect. You're not with me, are you? Angel's evil exists alright, but he doesn't know it, not yet, so it exists only as a potential. Sometimes, it spills out and confuses the hell out of him. You see, it's propelled by the forces other people created in him, put in the jug, it's not him. So each bit that comes out is kind of worse than the previous bit, but, and this is the difference between Angel and real evil people, when it comes out of Angel, it's out for good. The problem is, the worst bit is yet to emerge.'

'How, I mean, in what ways does it come out? And, how will you know, how will *he* know, when the worst is out?'

'He cheats, he tells terrible lies, he steals, he's not in charge of himself, he sets himself up to get hurt – he's already been gang raped once?'

34

'Raped? He set himself up?'

'Not consciously so, but make no mistake about it Poet, you stay on this scene for a year and you'll be raped at least once.'

'It's already happened once ages ago, in Liverpool, two guys in a public toilet, I was bleeding for a week. I got over it. But, how? I mean, how's he going to know when the last bit of evil comes out?'

'For God's sake Poet, you're as bad as he is! What do you mean, you got over it? What does that mean? How have you got over it?'

'You just have to don't you? You cope.'

'The hell you do! Don't you see anything? It stays, it fills the jug full of evil, full of hate, and if you don't do something about it, it'll rot your soul.'

'What can I do? I mean, it was ages ago.'

'You can put the blame where it belongs for a start!' He shouted, very angry.

'That's not as easy as you make out. I mean, if I hadn't been in there hustling, well, you know?''

'No I don't! Look Poet, the way you're going, you're going to be the first rent boy ever to get an 'A level' in Catholic guilt. You still don't get it do you?'

'You're beyond me Joker, you're like a philosopher or something.' I defended, mildly.

'I'm sorry, I'm on your side, I am sorry, straight. But, tell me this, did you ever sit down one day and say to yourself, I'm going to be a rent boy?'

'Of course not, it's not like that and you know only too well it isn't, don't you?' My question was real and I wanted an answer.

'Yes, I know! But, do you know why you're a rent boy?'

'I just figure I must be that way inclined, like the way I am about boys.'

'Jesus H. Christ! Being a rent boy is not a bloody orientation, it's a damn consequence. God, I'm bursting for a piss. Look, I'm not saying that everyone who gets sexually interfered with becomes a rent boy, or, for that matter, that every rent boy was interfered with when he was a kid, but don't you think it's kind of strange that you, Angel and me, all three of us, to use Actor's favourite word 'actually' were? Do you think it's a coincidence that Angel and me were in a kids home? Do you know how many rent boys were in kids homes? Take this flat, there's me and

Angel, and Magpie when he's around, in this room. In the next room, there's Biker and Flyer. I'm not sure about Banker. No one is. And, Actor, well he's come close enough, he got probation. And you, do you think it's another coincidence that your old man is a violent alcoholic? The hell it is. We're here because of what's gone before. We've become all consuming products and the only way out is to acknowledge the truth, beat the bastards at their own game, and become producers of our own identities. We have to empty the bloody jugs and fill them with what we want! Decide who we are and be it. Mess up their expectations. Now do you get it? Tell me you do, I can't cope much longer without a piss. Speak, brother speak.'

'I like the things that you say. I don't always understand them, but, hang on a minute, but, I think you're getting through to me, okay? You've got to be patient though, we're not all as bright as you, you know. 'Joker' indeed. But an 'A level' in Catholic guilt would look great on an application form, wouldn't it?'

As he dashed off to the bathroom, I heard him call,

'Terrific, what about an 'O level' in wanking?'

Whilst he was in the bathroom I tidied up the three beds and took the tea things back into the kitchen. It was all I could think of to do, to repay the gift I realised Joker had been sharing with me. I respected his passion, his sincerity. Just as I had finished cleaning up the kitchen, Biker came in, shivering in his underpants.

'Any tea on the go?' He asked, like a small kid.

'Yes, get some clothes on before you freeze to death and I'll pour some out for you. Do you want some toast?'

'Yeh, sound. Cut 'em into soldiers will yer?'

When he arrived back, clothed but still unwashed, like myself, Joker joined us and we sat around the gas cooker drinking tea and munching toast soldiers.

I picked up my conversation with Joker, though I kept it more general so as not to mention Angel. I sat close to Biker, by way of a welcome for him to join in. Which he acknowledged by handing around his cigarettes.

'Why do you think it is that kids can't always tell the difference between good and evil?'

Biker, aware that this must be part of a previous conversation, said nothing and listened with me to Joker's answer.

'You've seen those war films, you know, when one lot of

soldiers come across a scene of absolute bombed out chaos...'

'Like my fucking room, and Flyer's fucking head,' chipped in Biker.

'...and, there's all these bodies laying around. Then, one of the soldiers spots this diamond studded wristwatch on one of the bodies...'

'Not like my fucking room, after all...'

'...So, he goes over to it and starts to unfasten it, and it explodes in his face, and blows him and his mates to pieces.'

'I don't get it.' I said, truthfully.

'The fucking soldier did though, didn't he?' roared Biker. 'Splat!'

When the laughter died down, Joker continued.

'He was seduced into thinking that wealth lay there for the picking, you know, like that crap about the streets of London being paved with gold. Because it wasn't that obvious, he never even considered a boobytrap. Well, that's the way it is with kids, the evil which comes their way is usually all wrapped up and disguised as good.'

'It's dead fucking right, that. If you're going to attempt to con someone, you don't go in heavy handed and tooled-up, do yer? You smile and things, make 'em like yer. Then you rob 'em blind,' said Biker, intensely.

'Hole in one Biker,' rewarded Joker.

I knew somehow that he was right, but I said,

'You make it sound like the kids are absolutely innocent.'

'They are innocent, they're always innocent, until they've tasted and are corrupted by adult evil. Evil poured into their empty, innocent jugs, by evil adults, disguised as human beings, as parents, as teachers, as social workers. Kids are what adults make them.'

'Fucking hell, Joker, you been reading my kids home file, or what?' shivered Biker.

'They're all the same Biker, a tapestry of adult constructions, with individual bits about each of us so they can tell us apart.'

'They always knew who I was, I made fucking sure of that,' said Biker, to his teacup.

'Poet wasn't in a kids home, Biker.'

'Lucky bastard!' He spoke again to his teacup, then to me, 'You're on the run though?'

I nodded and knew that this was one of those times to remain

37

quiet, for something violent was brewing in Biker. His shoulders pulled in towards his chest, he sat rigid, his face changing from one person to another a thousand times. I wanted to put my arms around him but the signs said 'keep out'. I filled the cups with fresh tea and waited. For a long time he just stared ahead of him and I wanted to ask him where he was. Periodically, he shivered, though the heat from the gas oven had, by this time, warmed the kitchen. I glanced at Joker for instructions, he looked at Biker, gave me a reassured smile and, like me, waited for the eruption. Though he almost cracked his teacup with his ever tightening grip, it didn't come. As suddenly as he'd gone into his inner world of pain, he came out of it, laughed and said something about someone walking across his grave, and as proved to be his way, insisted on giving us more of his cigarettes. He so needed loving and was so unable to ask. Like many of us he found it easier to give but in his own unique fashion, as I would learn in time, he always gave too much. For the first time in my life I saw that outward aggression was no more than a cover for inner pain. Could my own father have been in this kind of pain? I risked putting my arm around his shoulders, very quickly sqeezed him, and then respecting his 'keep out' signs, withdrew just as quickly. He didn't pull away but turned to me and said,

'You're okay Poet.'

'So are you, Biker, so are you. And so is Joker, and so is Angel and I'm as lucky as anything to have met you, but don't expect tea and toast soldiers every morning, will you?' I said, joking.

'I tell you what, I'll take us out, Angel too if he'll sit still for two fucking minutes, tomorrow morning, for a slap-up breakfast, what do yer say? You on or what?' He beamed at Joker and I, as always going over the top.

By the time we'd stopped talking it was mid-afternoon and we all had a living to earn. Sensing the time, just as Angel had done earlier, we broke up and cleaned ourselves, ready for the street. A dirty kid does no business. Early and middle evening is rent boy time everywhere in the country. We didn't discuss going to the Dilly but we nonetheless headed there. I learnt how to jump the tubes without paying and on arriving at Piccadilly Circus, headed off on my own to find a phonebox. I had to call Alexander.

Before using the phone, I found a quiet corner, opened my pocket book at page two and, after much thought about the things Joker talked about, began to write:

Joker's Wild

Just
Occasionally
Kids
Enlist
Reason
So
Withstanding
Immutably
Learnt
Debauchery

Angelic Circles

Afterwards, I checked and double checked that I had the right amount of coins for the telephone, then checked again to be absolutely sure. Why was I delaying? Questions darted through my mind; would he expect me to call? How could our friendship hope to develop? Would he be there? Without having to check my pocket book for the number, I dialled, and waited. Almost instantly, the phone was answered:

'Hello?'

It was him!

'Hello, Alexander?'

'Yes, Scouse?'

'Yes, that was quick.'

'I've been sitting on the phone all day, afraid my father would answer. I thought you would never call. Where are you?'

'Piccadilly Circus. How are you?'

'All the better for hearing your voice. What are you doing there? Never mind. Can you come over? We're in Hampstead, do you know it?'

'When?'

'My parents are entertaining this evening, how about tomorrow morning? We could walk on the Heath?'

'Yes, what time?'

'Ten o'clock, at Jack Straw's Castle?'

'What?'

'It's a pub, can you find it?'

'Yes, yes of course.'

'I have to go, but I must tell you.'

'What? Don't go.'

'Walls have ears, I must go, I dreamt of you last night.'

'I'll see you at ten.'

The line went dead, but I hung on to the receiver, looking through it into his hazel eyes, wanting to climb down into the mouthpiece and out of the other end, into his arms. As conscious reality began to emerge in my soul, I began to realise that I must look faintly ridiculous, standing there staring at the telephone in my hand. I looked around to see if anyone was looking at me and put the receiver down. Ten o'clock at Jack Straw's Castle in Hampstead, yes.

As I made my way, reluctantly, towards the exit at subway number one I saw Angel with two well dressed men. Each of whom had a huge suitcase by his side. I stopped to watch and lit a cigarette. Angel was pointing to the suitcases and seemed to be indicating that they were too heavy. Did they want him to carry them? Surely not, for the men were themselves huge and looked fit enough. Unsure of whether or not to let Angel see me, I worked my way around so that I was in his, but not their, line of vision. When he saw me his face lit up and he called me over. As I got to him, so the men walked away, leaving the suitcases.

'What a sight for sore eyes,' he said, relieved.

'What's up? What are you doing with these?' I asked, indicating the suitcases.

'I need a favour or I'm in deep shit.'

'Name it, what's up? You're shaking.'

'So would you if you knew who that pair of brothers were.'

'Look, you're not going to understand this but I've got to get these on to the Circle line, smartish.'

'You don't need to explain anything unless you want to,' I said, grabbing hold of one of the suitcases, which proved to be as heavy as Angel had been indicating. 'What the Dickens is in here, do you know, or what?'

As we lifted, pulled, dragged, heaved, pushed and hauled the suitcases down the escalators to the Piccadilly line, then changed at South Kensington for the Circle, Angel began to put me in the picture and told me that there was a tenner in it for me.

He explained that it was something he did every now and again, to earn some money and keep the two brothers off his back. The brothers, one of them a homosexual very much into boys, ran a pornography racket from a variety of venues in and around Soho. Angel had met them when he did the homosexual one as a punter, in his first couple of weeks in London. It seems that they also had their fingers in other pies too, protection being uppermost.

'You've got to understand, Poet, these are not the kind of people you fuck about with.'

'Because?' I fished.

'There was this kid, a nice looking kid, from Manchester or some place. Anyway, he was on the rent scene and was picked up by the one into boys, and the kid ripped him off, you know? He lifted his watch and his wallet and pissed off. They cut his balls off for God's sake. Poet, they're ruthless.'

'How do you know, for sure?'

'Everyone knows about it, everyone on the scene anyway.'

'So why are you mixed up with the likes of them?'

'I'm not mixed up with them for God's sake. I just hump suitcases around and around the Circle line when they ask me to, for as long as they say. I get well paid and I don't ask questions.'

'So you don't know what's in them?'

'I can guess, it's got to be porn hasn't it? Magazines and things, you know? They're too heavy to be anything else, right? Look, they've got the Old Bill in their pockets. So, they know when the Woodentops are going to arrive, don't they? Have you any idea how many of these suitcases are going around on this line right now? They can't lose, see? I mean, if I get picked up by the Old Bill, I'm hardly likely to talk, am I? Not if I want to hang onto my wedding tackle, you with me?'

'Does Joker know about all this?' I asked, seriously concerned for Angel's safety.

'Dead right he does, we all do it. Well, not Banker, he's well in with them; he gets the boys for the pederast. It was Banker who introduced me to him.'

'A pederast? What's that?'

'That's the one one who likes boys. You know, like you and me? Young? A pederast is a man who's into boys, boys who are either just coming up to, or are just past, puberty. You with me?'

41

'Yes, I know about puberty, I looked it up in the dictionary, along with homosexual. You mean when we first grow hairs, right? I shaved mine off once.' I confessed, knowing I wouldn't be condemned.

'Everyone does! And our voices begin to get deeper, that's puberty, you've got it. But a pederast is not like a paedophile, they're different. And a homosexual is different again.' He went on, knowing he had a keen pupil.

'How do you know all this?' I asked, amazed at his articulacy.

'The kids home! There was a social worker there Alan, I used to do as a punter, right? He told me everything about sex. He was a pederast and he had loads of books, full of pictures, you know? Anyway, the paedophile, like I was saying, he's into boys and girls before they come anywhere near puberty.'

'Boys *and* girls?'

'Right!'

'Both the same?'

'Right!'

'But how? I mean, how can someone like boys and girls?' I asked, utterly confused.

'That's a paedophile, you tell me!'

'Jesus! That's weird. But is a pederast a homosexual?' I asked, even more confused.

'Some are, some aren't and not all homosexuals like boys, some of them prefer men their own age or even older. I've heard of men of sixty doing it with other men the same age.'

'At sixty!' I said, horrified at the thought.

'Sure, and then there's bisexuals. They like it with either a man or a woman.'

'Then they're paedophiles, right?'

'No, paedophiles only like little kids, boys and girls, before they hit puberty.'

'But then, let me get this straight, if paedophiles like both girls and boys, then they must be bisexuals, right?'

'Not really, because bisexuals like grown-ups better, well males and females who are already past puberty, anyway.'

'So what are the punters we do?'

'Mainly pederasts, like I said, and lonely homosexuals who can't get it up with people their own age. Then there's the homosexuals who are married, with kids of their own.'

'Married? What, homosexuals married?' I said, now completely lost. 'How? I mean, you're saying they have sex with women, but they prefer their own sex!'

'Hole in one Poet! It's simple enough to understand, these days, and it's always been like this, if you're a certain age and you're not married, and you've got a fancy job, well, people start talking, see?'

'But that must be terrible, having to have sex with a woman, when you prefer your own sex. I guess they must have to think about their own sex when they're doing it. Sometimes, I have to think about boys when I'm with a man, do you?'

'Loads of times. Joker does too.'

'So, what does that make us?' I said, slightly scared.

'We're all different, aren't we? Me? I think I'm 100% homosexual. What about you?' He asked, tentatively.

'I think so, I mean, I only ever think about my own sex, you know, when I wank and things.'

'Right, nothing wrong with it, right? Joker's the same. I've known him for ages, we're good mates. Then there's Biker, he's got a girlfriend. She stays at the flat sometimes, you know? And then there's Banker, he's a pederast but he works the scene too, to get the money to pay for his boys. I do him as a punter, sometimes. Then there's Flyer, you want to watch him, he takes drugs, he does it all, women's clothes, the lot. But he prefers women, really.'

'Women's clothes. Yea, I know about that.'

'For sure, some punters love that kind of thing,' he said, like the teacher he was.

'So what does that make Flyer, then, a bisexual?'

'Not really, he's more your transvestite type,' he said, glowing with knowledge.

He saw the question on my face, so continued.

'Your transvestite likes to dress in women's clothes but they nearly always prefer to have sex with women', though some do prefer men, and they're not transexuals.'

'What?' I almost screamed, 'You're making this up!'

'It's true, straight! Your transexuals would prefer to be the opposite sex!' He beamed, triumphantly.

'I'll never remember all this. You mean, there are people, men and women, who want to be the opposite to what they are?'

'And some of them have operations, you know, men have it all cut off and...'

'Stop!' I winced, and crossed my legs. 'It's like that kid you mentioned, the one who had his balls cut off. Was that for real?'

'Real enough. Let's change the subject, okay?' He said, quite sadly, all his confidence gone.

It had been fine to talk about anything other than what we were doing, going around and around the Circle line with two intimidating suitcases. Sex was always a good subject for boys such as us. Now I asked him where Hampstead was and if he knew of a pub called Jack Straws Castle. He told me that Hampstead was miles away, somewhere in north London but he'd never heard of the pub. It was understandable really, boys our age knew the names of picture houses and coffee bars, not pubs. Angel, pleased to be talking about anything other than the kid who'd been mutilated, went on to explain that I could get a tube map when we got off at St. James's Park station, a bit later.

A bit later, turned out to be much later. As much as I liked Angel, and I did, I was getting bored, and I was showing it. He worked hard to entertain me with jokes and stories of the kids home, and I did my best to tell him jokes and stories about growing up in Liverpool. In the end, we settled on stories about the war. Both of us having been born in the middle of it. At last, we had a bond, something to relate to. We were both 'war babies' of 1943 and as I discovered, we both loved everything American, especially American comics. What in the name of God were two war babies doing going around and around the Circle line?

Nine o'clock saw us emerge at St. James's Park and we stood by a bus stop, as though waiting. Twenty minutes later a car drew up and we loaded the suitcases into the boot and went to the window, where I saw the guy Angel had described as the pederast. He handed Angel a newspaper, winked at us, gave a friendly wave and took off in his flash car. Concealed in the newspaper was twenty quid, all in ones. We split the cash, and relieved of the worry and burden, skipped towards the Dilly like a couple of kids on holiday, singing Cliff Richard's hit, 'Move it'.

Come on pretty baby, let's move it and groove it.
Shake it baby, shake it honey, please don't lose it.
The rhythm that gets into your heart and soul, let me tell you, baby, it's
called rock 'n' roll.
They say it's going to die but honey please let's face it, they just don't
know what's going to replace it…

Angel knew just about everything there was to know about sex. Damn it, he could even spell the words! But his duality confused me. He was two people. At the centre of himself he was a tragic child caught up in something over which he had absolutely no control. I knew this for in that sense, we were brothers; just as he and Joker had become brothers. He even sang skipping songs and nursery rhymes. But he was, like so many of us, a skilled and mature craftsman. Angel crafted out of his experiences, a world in which he could control. It was a world I respected and could identify with, could live in, for it was simple and understandable. It was not a world of imagination and fantasy, for that, you see, was the real world. The world other people live in, Alexander's world! Angel's world, my inner world, were places where, well, you musn't laugh at this, it was where we became kings, cowboys or rock 'n' roll stars. As we skipped our way into Soho, we were Cliff Richard, as real as real could be, and Angel was better looking.

When I discovered that Angel didn't know of the Two 'I's coffee bar I was delighted. Here was my chance to be the teacher for a change. I explained how British rock 'n' roll owed its origins to the Two 'I's and that Tommy Steele and Cliff Richard had started out by singing there. Angel proved to be a better teacher than student for whenever he began to feel out of his depth, whenever he felt his crafted world was in danger, he changed the subject to sex. So it was that in order to explain anything further to him about rock 'n' roll I had to listen to twice as much about transexuals or the art of oral sex. It was a fair exchange, for there were no losers and both our inner worlds remained intact.

Indeed, had it not been for my insistence that he go with me, there and then to the Two 'I's, I might never have discovered 'fresh-cream-dip', and not knowing about this put me at least a year behind Angel in the rent boy knowledge stakes, just as his knowledge of rock 'n' roll put him about a year behind me. 'Fresh-cream-dip' is when the rent boy dips his erection into a pot of fresh cream and then offers this for the oral delights of the punter. Angel explained, quite seriously, that jam and honey could be used to the same effect but that cream was by far the best. I had to promise to tell him the first time I tried it.

To my great disappointment, Angel was already fully conversant with frothy coffee and ordered a cola instead. We were served by the owner of the Two 'I's himself, Tom Littlewood. He told us that Soho was the centre of the world but we knew that already. Tom left Leeds and came down to London in the early 50's and had made enough working as a stuntman in the movies to open the Two 'I's. With this, he had our full attention. We quizzed him about being a stuntman and about all the famous people he knew. We begged him to dish the dirt, give us the unreported gossip about the big names he knew so well. He put up a token resistance but eventually, after promises that we'd never tell a living soul, he played along with us and told us stories, stories we wanted to hear; and we sat and drank it all in, just as we drank in the endless colas and frothy coffees. I asked him what Cliff Richard was like.

'He's a nice kid. Got a future in the business but he won't go as far as Tommy Steele though, he copies Elvis the Pelvis too much. All he'll ever do is cover versions of American hits and there's no real future in that, see.'

'I think he's fantastic! The real thing! The best damn thing to happen to music in this country, ever! I mean, look at what's around, Lonnie- dinner-gong!' I protested earnestly.

Angel protested just as earnestly that skiffel would outlast rock 'n' roll any day. I gave way to his protest for fear that he might start on about oral sex.

On the way back to the flat by taxi (rent boys, Angel instructed, always take taxis when they can) I asked Angel to tell me more about the suitcases.

'There's nowt to tell, Poet, straight, the brothers grim give 'em to us, we cart the things around and we get paid for it. It's too dodgy to ask too many questions.' He instructed, indicatin that was the end of that subject.

I let it drop reluctantly and encouraged him to talk about sex. We slept together that night and experimented with fresh-cream-dip, which turned out to be rather messy, for not having cream, we settled for milk, instead. When he drifted into sleep I picked up my notebook and made my way into the kitchen to make my favourite drink, tea. From Biker's room came the inevitable sound of Radio Luxembourg and Cliff Richard singing his latest song, 'High Class Baby'. Opening my notebook I made some notes, which later turned out as this:

Angelic Circles

Against all this a
Nymph-like boy,
Greets a milky kiss,
Eloquently, existentialist.
London? A limp-like toy,
Intransigent and pissed,
Catalytically forms the
Canvas onto which,
Irradiated, unmissed,
Rent boys Coexist.
Living as a wheel,
Evidently circular and
Surreal.

Before going back to join the sleeping Angel I washed my under-
wear, shirt and socks then pinned a note on the kitchen door asking whoever was up first to give me a call.

As it turned out, my inner alarm clock woke me at about at
seven thirty so I took the note down myself. Lighting the gas oven,
I hung my clothes on the door to dry, whilst I took a luke warm
bath. Afterwards, in search of an iron, I looked in on my sleeping
flatmates. Joker was on his back, snoring lightly, whilst Angel was
curled into a little round ball in the middle of my bed. How many
times have I woken just like that? In the next room, Banker's bed
was empty, as was Flyer's. Biker lay curled and twisted as though
having a torturous nightmare. His blankets had been kicked to
the bottom of the bed, exposing his pale white naked skin. I
covered him up and put the blankets from Banker's bed over him
too. He groaned his sleepy gratitude and I was tempted to bend
down and kiss his cheek. In sleep, he looked the most vulnerable
of all those who shared the flat. Why only in sleep do our real
selves emerge? Sleep, it seems, is when our present and previous
garbage is somehow reconciled with our potential glory.

Actor's door, though closed, did not have the padlocks on, so
I opened it quietly and looked in. The room was neatly stacked
with boxes and cardboard containers all around the walls. It was
a veritable storeroom. Actor was asleep in a huge double bed in
the centre of the room. There was no iron but my eyes did fall on
four suitcases, exactly like the ones Angel and I had hauled

around the Circle Line. Weird, right? Dare I look? I wanted to very much, just a quick glance. It wouldn't be that difficult. Or, would it? The cases might be locked and I might wake Actor. I froze and tried to decide. What possible connection could there be between Actor and the brothers grim? What the hell did it have to do with me anyway? Actor, turning in his sleep, decided things for me. I left his room and closed the door as quietly as I'd opened it. I was, however, far more curious now than before, but I also felt bad about snooping about. I mean, the guy had let me stay in his flat, right? It was his business, not mine. But, Jesus, I was curious.

Hampstead proved not to be as far as Angel had suggested. I arrived there with over an hour to spare. Simple instructions from the ticket collector told me that I could be at Jack Straws Castle in less than fifteen minutes so I had time to kill before meeting with Alexander. I settled on a secondhand bookshop. An old man in a wide brimmed hat was laying out boxes of books, outside the shop. Each box had a little notice. I focused my attention on the box which had the sign, 'All in this box sixpence'. My fingers worked through the dusty pile until I saw a book explaining the origins of rhymes and sayings. I found that my fingers lingered there, telling my brain to pick up the book. I obeyed the call and flicked through the pages. Angel came to my mind as I heard his childlike voice singing. What was it he always sang? Yes, 'Girls and boys come out to play'. Yes, that's it. I searched the index and there it was on page 185.

> Girls and boys come out to play,
> The moon doth shine as bright as day,
> Leave your supper and leave your sleep,
> And join your playfellows in the street;
> Come with hoop, come with a call,
> Come and be merry or not at all,
> Up the ladder and over the wall,
> A half penny loaf will serve us all.

It seems that the content and meaning of the rhyme have always puzzled people. Why, the writer wanted to know, would kids be out 'playing' in the moonlight? A good question and one to which

I, and many other rent boys, had an answer to. In the seventeenth century, it seems, children were treated as miniature adults and because of this the writer then went on to postulate that perhaps the kids were 'playing' in the only spare time they had. Perhaps! But it felt like utter crap! And what, I asked myself, had changed between the seventeenth century and now? Kids were still treated as property, only some punters were more honest about purchase than many parents were. Nothing has changed! Kids are whatever adults make them, they are rarely themselves. I stared at the book and felt anger rise up inside me. I felt that I was holding a book as deviant as any I'd seen around in Soho. I flung it on the pile and stormed off, telling myself that one day I would do something to help rent boys be understood better, both by themselves and others. I headed for Jack Straws Castle with the rhyme ringing in my ears. Damn that tune, I couldn't shake it.

I arrived at the pub with half an hour to spare, so I brought out my notebook knowing, that to rid my head of the tune, I had to get it out, onto paper. So, I wrote my own version of 'Girls and boys come out to play'.

> *Young rent boy come out to stay,*
> *The Dilly doth shine as bright as day,*
> *Leave your self and risk the gleet,*
> *Join the punters in Glasshouse Street;*
> *Come with skill, come in a thrice,*
> *Come and be bought but watch the price,*
> *Down with trousers and up with shirt,*
> *Is this the night that you get hurt?*

I got the word 'gleet' from who else but Angel. It means a gonorrhoea discharge. But to Angel it also meant the kind of punter one wouldn't be seen dead with. Mr Gleet was working class, unwashed, unkempt, drank beer by the bucket full, had bad breath and represented everything a rent boy wanted to avoid. He was, according to Angel, the kind of person most likely to have VD and should therefore be avoided at all costs. VD was something I knew absolutely nothing about yet feared terribly. I'd have to ask him to talk more about it. Indeed, so ignorant was I about VD that I thought one could only get it from women, though I fortunately hadn't said as much to Angel.

'Hello, have you been here long?'

That voice! It was Alexander! The angry rage, which my version of the rhyme evoked within me, bounced off the beautiful sound of his voice. I stared at him, my emotions bouncing backwards and forwards like a table-tennis ball. Speak! For Christ's sake say something! I fumbled to put my notebook away, taking in his sparkling hazel eyes. He was smiling and offering me his hand. I took it. Its silky smoothness sending shivers up and down my spine. He was speaking again:

'This is my sister, Verity. Verity, this is Scouse; and this, Scouse, is Tramp.' He said, indicating a small shaggy dog. 'Shall we walk?'

I shook hands with Verity and mumbled something about being pleased to meet her and only having been there a short time. My eyes searched Alexander's. Why had he brought his sister? The dog I could understand but his baby sister. He acknowledged my silent questions with a shrug of his shoulders. He obviously felt bad about it.

We walked as a group on to Hampstead Heath and Alexander let Tramp off his lead. Then, picking up a stick, he threw it. Tramp chased it and brought it back, dropping it at our feet, inviting us to continue the game. Alexander obliged a number of times and then let his sister take over the central role. As she played happily with the equally friendly animal we moved a couple of yards away and sat on the cold grass.

'My mother insisted I bring her.' He spoke softly, his eyes following the girl. 'What could I do?'

'I'm glad you came, with or without your sister.'

'Are you? I'm furious about it! You mean that?' He asked, his eyes searching mine for... for comfort?

'Yes I am, don't be mad about it. Whatever the circumstances, I simply feel good to see you.'

'What were you writing? You were so engrossed in it. He asked, as though relieved.

'Oh, just a bit of poetry.' I said, dismissively. 'Notes really,' I could hardly say nursery rhymes could I?

'May I see?' He asked, glancing at his watch.

'I'll send something to you, something special, okay? When do you have to be back?'

To my utter relief the suggestion that I'd send something

seemed to please him, but I now faced the task of writing something 'special'.

'By eleven I'm afraid. Let me give you my address? Do you write much?'

'Not as much as I'd like to.'

I offered him a blank page from my notebook, and prayed that he wouldn't ask for mine. As he wrote his name and address in precise schoolboy writing he said, as though reflecting to himself;

'Something special.' Then, gathering his thoughts more, he continued, smiling, 'Our meeting was a special express you know.'

'The train?'

'Yes, the train, a special train, our train.' He laughed. 'Do you like trains? I adore them. Steam trains, that is. Had I been allowed my wish we'd have taken the later one, The Red Rose. It has fourteen coaches. Our train, The Merseyside Express, only had thirteen, but I shall never forget it, not now. I adore steam trains like The Merseyside and The Shamrock, but that left too early for us; at 8.05am, getting into London at 12.15pm. And we nearly took the Great Western to Paddington. Oh, we could have missed each other, so easily. My father wanted us to take the new English Electric Prototype, do you know it? The Deltic? Well, it's a diesel electric and my father says that it's the future train. I managed to talk him out of it. Imagine, a smelly diesel?'

I was entranced with his enthusiasm for steam trains. He became completely animated the more he spoke. I asked questions and he responded with the expert knowledge that Angel had about sex. He spoke of the unique sounds and shapes of engines; of the richness and quality of the ride; of the individual nature and rhythm of each locomotive.

'Some people can distinguish one engine from another, just by the rhythm and movements.' He enviously enthused.

Verity came over to join in the talk but headed off again quickly with the comment, 'Not trains again!'

Alexander took not the slightest notice of her, except to say, 'Girls!'

I could have listened to him all day, but somehow, just thinking about time brought it all to a halt. Alexander glanced at his watch and I cursed inside.

'Gosh, look at the time! We must dash or there will be hell to pay. You will send me the *something-special*?'

'You can bank on it.'

I left them at the far side of the Heath and watched them head for their happy home. Reluctantly, angrily, I made my way back to the tube station and Soho.

Alexander's world, so far from my own, was the world I'd avidly read about in childhood comics. A beautiful world of well fed kids and public school; of close friendships and secure families; of long glorious summer holidays and crisp white shirts. Was I attracted to Alexander or his world? I think both. I didn't envy him for what he and his family actually had but I did feel very angry at the visible differences between our two worlds. Was that so bad? Why was there such a divide? Why do some of us have drunken violent fathers and some not? Why do some kids end up in kids homes and some in public schools? Why the hell wasn't I in some damn bookshop buying books on the things which mattered to most boys, things like steam engines and sport? Why did I sense that Alexander and I were hopelessly inappropriate?

Was I so like the jug Joker talked about, full with the evil of others? I mean, he was right when he'd said that I'd never sat down and said to myself, 'I think I'll be a rent boy!' And that's why not being one anymore wasn't just a matter of saying to myself, 'I think I'll stop being a rent boy now!' Or, am I just making excuses for being fundamentally immoral? I mean, has my moral will sunk into the jug of evil and fuelled my own compost? Can a person BE evil? Or, is evil something external which influences and rots the living soul from the outside? Is the soul that fragile? I wanted to be a happy boy in a happy family. I wanted to go to a happy school and do happy things. I wanted to have time to be interested in steam engines. I wanted to be a good boy. So why wasn't I? Why was I so many people all rolled into one? This, or the other. Am I myself, or just a paid lover? Am I what some say I am? Or am I the spaces in between the words they use to describe me? Is that the way people are? A mixture of hopes and dreams, of good and bad, of sorrow and searching? Why does sadness always dominate serious thought? So many questions, so many *why's* bounce endlessly around between my heart and my head.

Passing the secondhand bookshop once again, I stopped to look at the book I'd thrown down earlier. Picking it up I wrote my version of the rhyme directly over the printed version and carefully placed the book back. Delinquent, right? Not the kind of thing a good boy would do.

Two weeks after starting work on the poem, locked away in the local library, and having done only a few punters, I enclosed my real name and the flat address and sent Alexander the following piece:

Something Special

Something special,
Our vessel self,
Moving, sensual,
Erotic wealth;

Therein reflects,
Hellenistic light,
Impenitent depths,
Nimbus bright;
Gamin and lord,
Sceptre and dove,
Procryptic sword,
Epyllion love;

Cassandra waits,
Inviolate twin but,
Apollo placates the,
Labyrinthian.

On the reverse side of this I wrote out the other piece called 'Alexander'; the one which had earned me the nickname Poet. Would he understand? I could merely wait and let my mind play with an endless fantasy:

...His love of trains, whose loss whose gain? His talk of steam, his engine my dream, twixt and between; impossible hopes made fast with ropes, spun by him and spun by me, cords of class and family. Drunk or sober, father and mother, the paid disrober would rather the other... Why do I torture myself so?

Flyer's Party

F lyer's party was going to be the best damn drag ball that London had ever seen and everyone in the flat had been recruited to make it so. Everyone had been invited, rent boys and rent girls, transvestites and transexuals, drag queens and lesbians, young and old. Everyone was supposed to drag up for the party, boys as girls and girls as boys. Above all else, it had to be absolutely outrageous. I was terrified!

Fortunately for me my terror was shared by Biker who made it clear that 'there was no fucking way he was going to put a fucking dress on, not for any fucker!' I echoed his views and joined him in masculine protest. The others, however, having found a greater unity in each other's desire to dress up, worked on Biker and me right up to the night itself. Biker's last words on the subject, as the party got under way, perhaps predictably were, 'No fucking chance!'. A couple of hours and a few beers later, Biker and I looked pretty good in our makeshift grass skirts and bare chests. We even did a dance together. It was a hell of a party! It was simply a matter of grabbing hold of the joy while it was there, grab it, join it, or miss it. Everyone who came, and there were plenty, all brought booze. Some had reefers, but I gave them a miss, more out of fear than knowledge.

Even though we knew Banker was 'getting off' on it, Biker and I allowed him to talk us into covering our faces, torsos and legs with some of Flyer's make-up. To make us 'look more like natives'. What the hell, it was a party. Or, to put it in Biker's own words, 'Fuck it! Do it man!' And do it he did. Locked in the bathroom, he could hardly contain himself as we stood before him, grass skirts thrown to one side, in our underpants. He did Biker first, for reasons which became clear when he managed to get Biker back out into the party. Alone in the bathroom he stood and knelt before me rubbing the stuff into my skin.

'It might be better if you took your briefs off?' He suggested, his eyes focused on them.

'Do me a favour Banker, I know what you're after.' I laughed, in party mood.

'I was just thinking that the edges might get stained…around here…and here…' He said, touching my skin just under the edges of my underpants. 'Look, its just that... You're a nice boy... Lovely smooth skin...I'll pay you... Here...' He said, almost pathetically, producing the money. 'Shame to stain your white briefs...Let me help you off with them...'

I remembered what Angel had told me about doing Banker as a punter so I took the money and felt my briefs being pulled down to my ankles. He took me in his mouth and I had great difficulty getting a hard-on as I looked down at the young man in drag sucking my limp cock. The limpness, however, seemed to please him, give him something to work on, I guess. He proved to be an expert at what he was doing and I soon, despite my own amusement, became hard. I came without too much of a problem but without any real interest. Afterwards, he pleaded with me not to mention what had happened to the others, telling me he would pay more next time and introduce me to people with 'real money' to spend on a nice young boy like me.

I went back into the party, found Angel and told him that I'd just done Banker as a punter.

'Nice one Poet, without having to go out for it eh?' He laughed. 'Bet he was all sorry afterwards? He always is. His kind always are. Where'd you put the money?'

'Where do you think.' I said, gropping beneath my grass skirt and snapping the top of my underpants against my belly.

'That should keep them warm! Wanna dance with lady?' He asked, taking my arms and dancing.

'You look ridiculous!' I shouted, over the music. 'Where did you get that frock, from a jumble sale?'

'You should talk! You haven't looked in the mirror yet have you? Besides if that's the way you intend to address a lady, she'll have no other choice but to smack you in the gob! Now wiggle your arse and dance!'

I danced, happily and long into the night and fell asleep with the party still going on around me.

I woke at around noon the next day to find Biker, his girlfriend, Angel and a huge lesbian friend of Joker's all asleep in or over my bed. The room was full of snoring bodies and had that after party smell to it; stale beer and wine all wrapped up in ashtray scent. Those on and in my bed, and the bed itself were covered in more make-up now than I had on me. I felt wonderful and allowed myself to drift back into that contented state of half-sleep.

Someone was banging on the front door of the flat and a voice was shouting, 'Get the flippin' door, for God's sake.' The door was opened and voices filtered through the flat. 'It's for someone called Richie! Is there anyone here called Richie? It's Alexander somebody for someone called Richie.' I flew out between, around, over and on the stirring bodies and dashed into the hallway. The hallway, too, had become a dormitory and I danced between the sleeping figures of at least ten Miss Worlds and came face to face with a tall well dressed man. I knew his face but...

'Are you Richie McMullen?'

'Who wants to know? Who are you?' I countered, confused, still half asleep.

He pulled a piece of paper from his pocket and waved it at me. 'Are you the...author...of this...filth?'

'What the hell are you talking about? What filth?'

He thrust and I grabbed the piece of paper and it took just a fraction of a second to realise that it was the piece I'd sent Alexander.

'Where did you get this? Who are you? I asked, knowing the answer, already.

'I don't know how you met him but you, and I can see what kind of...person...you are... He mocked, looking around at the now fully awake figures. 'You're under age for... all of this...You sent that filth to my son. It seems to me that the police would have a serious amount to say about whatever it is that goes on here. How old are you? You and your kind should be locked up!'

At the sound of this all hell broke loose, people dashing about, gathering belongings, getting out of drag, cursing me to get rid of him.

'You don't understand...' I begged.

'You're damn right I don't. Look at you! Have you... touched my son?'

Of course not! My poem, my...*inviolate twin*... If you've read it...you'd see...

'Poem? Pornography!'

'Please, I'm sorry, honestly. It was not meant for your eyes...'

'Of course not! It is not uncommon...in decent families...for a son to have the same name as his father. If I ever set eyes upon you ever again McMullen, or if you ever try to contact my son I'll thrash you within an inch of your life.'

'You'll have to go through me first to do it pal!' said Biker as cool as ice.

'Biker please, stay out of this.' I turned to plead and there was Angel and Joker standing either side of Biker.

'All for one and one for all Poet. Get the fuck out of here pal...' Biker grinned menacingly and produced a knife, '...go on, before I rip your bleeding guts out and piss on your fucking insides.'

It was ridiculous, there was Biker clad in grass skirt flanked by two boys in frocks, defending me. I wanted to burst out laughing. Or was it crying?

'You've not heard the last of this! Damn perverted queers!' He stormed out and Biker kicked the door shut behind him.

'Forget it Poet! You've seen the last of him, cunt!', said Biker trying to comfort me as Angel wiped my unashamed tears.

'Come on Poet...' said Angel, 'rent boys don't cry.'

'Who the hell was he anyway?' asked Joker, taking the piece of paper from my hand. 'Oh shit! I'm sorry, Poet.'

'Actually, so am I...actually,' chipped in Actor. 'How did he get this address? And he knew your proper name for God's sake! I'm sorry Poet but it's out of order, actually. The last thing we all need, actually, is the Old Bill calling for tea, if you get my drift? I mean, it's not fair on the others is it? And it means that I've actually got to...unload... certain items quickly. No doubt some other people will need to unload other...items...Flyer? People, certain...other˙...people, are not going to be at all pleased, actually, if you get my drift?'

My world was caving in all around me. I wanted to scream at Actor to shut up but I knew he was right˙. I had no right to put others at risk. What I'd done had lacked thought and consideration. I told Actor that he was right, that I was genuinely sorry and that I'd move out just as soon as I got washed and dressed. Everyone pleaded with Actor but it was a token of affection for they knew too that he was right.

When I was just about to leave Banker shoved some money in my hand with a piece of paper, telling me to take care. I thanked him and I agreed to meet Angel and Joker later, down at the Dilly.

An hour later I stood on the meat rack in Glasshouse Street, cold lonely and sick to my stomach that I'd lost Alexander. I wanted to die. What now? Now I had to stand on my own two feet and survive London, that's what!

Tennis John

W hat is it about the pain of isolation which prevents a boy from feeling the cold? Perhaps, it's just that the cold inside is colder than the cold outside. While other people shiver to keep warm, the Dilly-boy thinks and dreams to keep warm. He thinks of lost loves. He dreams up the fires of imagined love. He feels its warmth wrap his dreams with absolute protection. He dreams of what might be. But, because he's thinking his dream, he knows it's all make believe and, like everyone else, he too eventually shivers out the truth. Damn the truth! The truth is I'd rather be here alone, in the cold, in a strange city, on the game, than back in Liverpool, with my father.

Hail Mary full of grace, the Lord is with thee, Blessed art thou amongst women, and Blessed is the fruit of thy womb, Jesus.' Damn! Damn! Damn! These prayers lash my inner self with such regularity that I want to scream out loud for them to stop. They never do. They always know when to attack, they wait until I'm a bit down, a bit depressed, and then creep up on me, burst through my defences and sing their song of triumph in my consciousness. At fifteen years old the Catholic messages are carved on the inside of my bones, they live there, knowing they're safe from challenge, and while they're there I can not become free. They dominate my spiritual identity and I am their prisoner, locked away from self, unable to decide who I am. My mother's powerful words echo in my head, 'Once a Catholic, always a Catholic!' But she's wrong, she has to be wrong. If she's right, then I'm trapped forever. Trapped in a kind of imposed living death. It's like my self is pushed to one side, cast out, and this other bit takes over. It's like I don't exist anymore and my mind has been taken over by an outside force. The force is supposed to be good because it's supposed to be God or something but it just doesn't feel like that so it can't be good, can it? I mean, if it's good, then why do I feel so bad? I figure it's because my true self just doesn't have room to grow in, if you know what I mean. I mean, if someone else decides who we are then we just die off. I get so confused because I don't know which bit is me, you know? I know Joker would understand, but I don't know if I'll ever see him again. Adults don't help, they seem to stop asking questions when they get old. They just give in.

Questions torment me. How is it possible for something bad to emerge out of something good? The poetry I sent Alexander was good, I don't mean the poetry as poetry, but more the intention. Yet, look what happened, look at the result. I don't know, it just caves my head in to think about it.

Searching my pockets for a cigarette, the note Banker shoved into my hand comes to my attention. It turns out to be a name and a telephone number. I feel grateful for something to take my mind off things, and forgetting that I'd arranged to meet with Joker and Angel, I decide there and then to telephone. Anywhere is a better place to be. His name is John and he tells me to take a taxi to the address he gives me, he'll pay when I get there. Suits me!

He's about forty-five or so, thin on top, pleasant, educated, slightly nervous, wears glasses and he smokes non-stop. He has jerky hand and body movements which remind me of the actions of a child who has just been discovered doing something wrong. His flat is huge, furnished tatsefully and centrally heated. After being shown around we head for the huge kitchen. He prepares lunch and there is no mention of sex. Instead, he tells me that his passion in life is tennis, that he was educated at a public school and that he works in the Youth Service. His willingness to talk so freely puts me at ease and I listen as this strange and delicate man makes himself more and more vulnerable. I know that he's a punter, he knows that I know he likes boys, yet still no mention of sex. I figure that he's a talker, I've met them before. They just talk and pay well. He tells me everything about himself, his family, his love of tennis, his work, even of his attraction to boys, but he never asks me a question about myself. He chatters on, preparing food and drinking wine, as though we'd known each other for a lifetime. I listen and watch. He keeps his distance, not invading my space.

Lunch is five first rate courses, each with a different wine. He talks, I listen. We are both content with the arrangement. As the wine takes effect, I ask him questions about tennis, which he is delighted to answer. He is a perfect host, paying attention to my every need. I enjoy his talk, his voice, the classical music in the background. All the non-verbal signals are of safety, relaxation, security, endless time, comfort, wealth and pleasure. I don't allow my mind to wander hours into the past. Instead, helped by the wine, I celebrate the present and let my mind wander into the future. I imagine a life like this, a comfortable home of my own.

Is it all so much to ask?

It becomes clear to me that what pleases John is being close to a boy, watching him, being around him. Sex, if it is to happen, will be initiated by me. So, when he tells me that I can stay just as long as I want, and that I can have my own room, I accept. I like him, he's not pushy and that makes me want to please him. In the evening after a shower, I drape a towel around me and wander through the flat, drying my hair. I can see that he's pleased. His eyes do the touching, and not his hands. I enjoy showing off my boy-body to his appreciative delight and I let the towel slip from my waist. I stand before him, naked, and offering him the towel, ask him if he'll dry my hair and my back for me. He does so, gently, like the caring man he obviously is. He senses my needs and tells me that I am beautiful. As he does so, our needs melt into each other, like butter into hot toast. There is no sex, just two vulnerable people gaining strength from each other. I thank him and go off to bed. Five minutes or so later he brings me a hot milk drink and leaves me, telling me to 'sleep warm'. I do.

In the morning I wake to find a note, keys to the flat, and some 'pocket money'. Had he gained the same pleasure, looking at me in my sleep, as I had looking at Angel? I hoped so. The note explained that he'd gone to his office and that he'd be home again about seven in the evening. I phone Alexander to discover he's moved.

In Oxford Street, later, the 'pocket money' buys me a new pair of jeans, a shirt, a pair of white tennis shorts, a white tennis shirt, white socks and white tennis shoes, which, I figure, I'll wear around John's flat. With more than enough 'pocket money' over I head for the Two 'I's coffee bar, with the intention of later going on to the Dilly afterwards to share my new found wealth with Joker and Angel. After two hamburgers and two frothy coffees I take out my note book and write:

Tennis John

Tentative whole with Peter Pan soul,
Enriched by the boy, the didicoy boy.
Naturalistically fuelled, and
Nonsense de-schooled, he
Invites me to share my wet blond hair, then

Shining, the prize, his delicate eyes, when
Joining my needs he wordless agrees
Our need
for the other, not like the lover, but
Halcyon calm with extended arm he creates with grace,
Non-targetted space, in which I flow, in which I flow.

Thumbing through my notebook, I read the pieces inspired by
Alexander and fail to find the pornography his father found there.
Could it be that I am blind to my own negativity? Or is Alexander's
father simply scared of his own imagination?

In my notebook thumbing, I see Joseph's name and his army
address and decide to drop him a line. Whilst doing so, I reflect
on the rib-poking fun, the sharing of his meat pie, his cigarettes,
his money, his warm regard for my safety in London and the dirty
jokes. Using John's flat address, I tell Joseph that I've found a
place to live and that London is no big deal. On the way to the
Dilly I post the letter, not daring to expect a reply.

At The Meat Rack my thoughts become occupied with Actor
having to 'unload' certain items from the flat, just in case the
police 'actually' arrive. I should have looked in those cases, in his
room, when I had the chance. The chances are though, that they
all contain porn, right? Fear grips me, instantly. You see, if they
do contain porn, then the brothers grim could be after me at this
very moment. This is no time to be hanging around, so I head for
the tube and make my way back to Tennis John's.

As I always tend to do when under any kind of pressure or when
I feel dirty inside, I take all my clothes off and shower. The water
which licks my wounds and kisses my skin reminds me of those
tender times when my mother bathed me as a child. As the water
wraps my body in warmth, I first hum then sing my private
version of a popular folk song:

Now boys are a-pleasing, and men are a-teasing,
And sex is a pleasure, when first it's new,
But as it gets older so sex gets a-colder,
And fades away like the morning dew.
I wish, I wish, I wish in vain,
I wish I were quite pure again,

But pure again I ne'er can be,
Till apples grow on an orange tree.

Now renting is easy, and renting does free me,
And money is power, the more I make,
But as I get more wealth so I get poor health,
And risk the grave by my first mistake.

I wish, I wish, I wish in vain,
I wish I were quite pure again,
But pure again I ne'er can be,
Till apples grow on an orange tree.

When John telephoned to say that he would not be home until very late, I was already dressed in the tennis whites. He told me where to find some cash and to go out and enjoy myself. I can't explain it all that clearly, but I guess I was disappointed that I couldn't show off the outfit. Still, he could see me tomorrow. Leaving the tennis whites on my bed, I slipped into my new jeans and shirt, almost drowned myself in John's best after shave, checked that the flat was secure and headed for the West End to see a film. I couldn't bring myself to take anymore cash though, besides, I had enough over from the 'pocket money' to last me the evening. Anyway, deep inside I felt kind of rich.

It was only as my feet hit the pavements of the West End that fear returned. Angel's story, of the boy the brothers grim had mutilated, sent yet another shiver down my spine. Had Alexander's father told the police about the flat? Probably. Then, what had become of Joker and Angel? If they were picked up, they'd be taken back to the kids home. Or, even worse, taken to separate kids homes. And it would all be my fault. I had to find out. To hell with the pictures, I had to see for myself.

I searched the West End for them, asking other street kids if they knew either Joker or Angel. Nothing! I waited around The Meat Rack for a couple of hours. Still nothing! There was only one thing left to do. I had to go to their flat in Earl's Court. Actor answered the door,

'Well, who'd have thought you'd actually have the nerve to turn up here...'

'...Look Actor, I'm sorry, honestly. I wouldn't have come but

I need to know...'

'...What happened?'

'Yes.'

'Nothing, actually.' He said, folding his arms across his chest.

'What do you mean? What about Joker and Angel?'

'Gone!'

'Actor, please.'

'Actually, they packed their bags and left, with Biker, and went off to some squat in Islington. Don't ask me where, I don't actually know. But, I'll tell you this, you rent boys are actually more trouble than you're worth and considering I opened up my home to you...'

'...Islington?'

'I told you, I don't know where. They took *my* teapot too, and *my* pans, and *my* blankets, bloody thieves. Yes, Islington! And when you see them, tell them from me, not to come back.'

'What about the police? Did they actually come?' I pleaded to know, using his favourite word in an attempt to ease things.

'Actually, no. No thanks to you, *actually*.' He countered, using the last actually to cut me with.

'Did you unload the gear?' I asked genuinely concerned.

'That's for me to know and you to guess, actually.'

'I said I was sorry, and I am, straight up, honestly.'

'Well, we'll leave it at that then.'

'I don't want any trouble, Actor. I'm going to be straight with you, I'm scared shitless of someone coming after me about all this...'

'Actually Poet, you're worried about nothing, so forget it. As I said, we'll leave it at that.'

'You mean no one's looking for me?'

'Not that I know of, apart from your mummy and daddy. Like I said, Poet, nothing happened, no police, no one looking to cut you up, nothing. The man was all mouth, and knows that if he brings the police in he'll have to explain things, right? And a gent like him wants nothing to do with the police. So, put it down to experience and think before acting next time, okay? Oh, and by the way, tell Angel he owes me a week's rent and tell Biker the teapot was due for the bin anyway. And Poet, look after yourself, okay.'

'Thanks Actor, you're a pal. I won't forget this, thanks.'

He smiled and winked as he closed the door. Despite his earlier justified anger at all the fuss I caused, Actor was letting me off the hook. I knew, and he knew that I knew, that had he wanted, he could have made my life in London hell. He was okay.

Waiting for Friends

In the centre of my very soul I have come to learn what Joker meant about Angel becoming more like a brother. It's not just that I miss them both. It's that their absence diminishes my own existence. I feel incomplete, fragmented without them.

So, I wait around the meat rack for them to appear, to make me whole again. My imagination tells me that they too are incomplete without me, though I don't stay with that thought for long. I'm afraid, you see, that they don't need me as I need them. Biker, too, is now part of me. I hear his voice in my head, the constant use of that four letter word now has warmth to it. I feel my lips move to pronounce it. It's not the same, it lacks his passion. But it's Joker and Angel I want to see more than anyone else. I need Joker's wisdom and Angel's uncomplicated loving. I wait, one day, two days, three days. I become part of The Meat Rack, turning down punter after punter. I've almost set up home on the Rack and Tennis John has seen very little of me. He is concerned. I tell him that I'm waiting for friends. The days and evenings merge into one blur and I forget which is which, so bright the lights around the Rack. Anxiety takes over from depression as I imagine them being hauled off to kids homes, or being picked up by the police. I hear them talking to each other, telling each other what a damn fool Poet was. I see myself being relegated to past tense in their conversations. It's late, very late.

I sit on the now closed newspaper seller's box, draw my knees up to my chest and let my head fall in fitful bouts of sleep. I fear I'll never see them again. Punters hover, attracted by my increasing vulnerability. I pretend not to understand what they're after. I ignore them. I drift deeper into sleep, exhausted by the wait. How long has it been? A week? Two? I don't care. I hope the police pick me up, I deserve no better. Joker and Angel are most likely in some damn kids home anyway. I don't care what becomes of me now. I give up. I don't even feel afraid as I feel all my inner defences begin to fall. I ache for my friends. I stop going back to Tennis John's at the end of the day, or is it night? I hang around the Rack fearing that the moment I leave is the moment they might show up. I stop eating and find myself having to bum cigarettes and the odd cup of coffee. Defences all gone, an empty belly, terrible depression at the loss of friends, I hear myself agreeing to go with a punter.

I don't pay attention to his talk, or his car. He takes me to a cafe and while I'm in the toilets vomiting up a green nothing, he orders me a meal and some coffee. I pick at the meal but drink the coffee in one gulp. He orders more, I drink it. I don't look at his face, he's just a punter, end of story. In his car I feel kind of sick again, feel myself drifting off into a weird kind of sound filled sleep. A sleep where I'm aware of all that's going on around me. Shapes become distorted, sounds have a strange kind of echo to them, colours become bright, dancing bright. I hear the punter saying we've arrived and feel myself being helped from the car. We enter, what? Not a house, not a flat. It's like a huge empty factory. I fall through the dancing colours and the punter's laughter, deep, deep into sleep.

The first thing I see when I wake is the handcuffs on my wrists, then my nakedness, the chains around my ankles and around my throat. I jump instantly with fear, pulling and screaming without sound, for I am gagged. Terror fills me. All my unspoken fears of being a rent boy are here. I struggle and pull at the restraints and fall in the attempt, drained of energy. I sense the space around me, though wherever I am is barely visible. I talk to myself, in my head, in an attempt at calming myself. I can't focus my thoughts though, for fear and terror dominates. I know I am about to die and I can't do anything about it. Then I freeze, quite motionless, as I see the figure coming towards me. He stops, just out of vision and speaks;

'You will do as I say. If you hesitate I will be forced to kill you. You will do whatever I say, when I say, and if you please me you may get to live. If you don't obey me, then you will die. Do you understand? I said, do you understand?'

I nod my head for all I'm worth! I believe every word he says. I must survive. I will do anything to survive, anything. I'm at the hands of a total nutcase and I can guess what's coming. But I will survive, I will. I continue to nod my head for fear he's not seen me the first time. I force myself to think, *I will survive!* Just do what he wants, anything is better than death, just do it. Just tell yourself you're waiting for friends and this is just a daydream. It will all be over soon. Damn it, it's just a bad dream, you'll wake up soon and it will all be over.

About two days later, after vile experiences and total humiliation I wake to find that all the restraints are gone, my clothes stacked beside me, and on top of them, a pile of one pound notes. Still gripped with fear, and believing this to be just another part of his disgusting game, I dress slowly and make my way tentatively into the shadows, looking for a way out. Once outside, I run faster than ever in my life. Even when my chest is bursting, I continue to run. People look at me strangely and I run even faster. Can they see what's just happened? I think so. I run and I run, putting as much distance between me and that place as I can. Eventually, I collapse into a screaming crying heap and people gather around me, asking what's wrong. A man offers me his hand to help me up and I curse him to the depths of hell and tell him to take his disgusting filthy hands from me. I get up and I run some more. When I eventually come to my senses I discover I'm in the East End of London, near the docks. The sights and sounds remind me of Liverpool, so I stay there for a long time, trying not to think, waiting for friends. But, think I do. I think that I can't go to the police. They won't believe me. Besides, how could they? I mean, who could believe a rent boy on the run from home? I couldn't even find that place if I tried. No more than I could describe either the man or his car. Was I drugged? I'm not even sure about that now. But the important thing is, I did survive. I am alive to tell the tale. But, to who? Who would want to hear it anyway? Still I am alive, I am alive, I am alive. The realisation that I'd come through the experience pulsed its message through my consciousness. So *live, live, live*. Get the hell out of here and live. Find Joker, find Angel, and live. They would understand, only they could understand. Only they could help me cope with the anger and hate, only they could prevent me from turning those emotions in on myself. I must get to them before this inner feeling of dirt and self blame engulfs me forever. What is it Joker says, empty the jug out, don't let others fill your jug for you, empty it out and fill it with what you want to be inside. But what's in there now is anger and hate and thoughts of revenge, terrible violence, and I want them to stay there, always.

Tennis John asks no questions, and I almost wish he would so that I can pour out the horror of what took place. Instead he simply tends to me, while I stay in my bed for over a week. When he goes out to work or whatever, I talk to myself, so as not to feel dirty, guilty or to blame. Over and over I tell myself that the responsibility belongs solely to the man who raped me. Joker would be proud, if he could hear me. I hear Joker's voice in my head, '...You can start by putting the blame where it belongs...' So I do. I curse the man at the top of my voice. I write it all down and set fire to the paper. I never did decide that I'd be a rent boy, so I do not accept responsibility for what results from it. Damn it, even if I do accept that I am what I am through an act of free will, no one has the right to rape me, right? Damn right! I swear, if I ever see the man again I'll kill him.

I punch the hell out of the pillows and bed. I beat him to death. Then, exhausted by it all, I cry myself to sleep, ashamed that I cry so easily. When I wake, I tell myself not to allow that man to dictate what I feel, let alone what I do. I realise that the problem is not mine, but his. I must not become like him. I must not hate or abuse my violent potential. I must not ever rely upon violence, or the threat of it, to achieve my aims. I must dictate what it is that goes into my jug, just like Joker said. And the last thing I want in there is violence. I've had just about all I can take of that human activity. I don't know if I'll be able to tip out all the violence, hate and desire for terrible revenge, but I do know that I'm sure as hell going to do my best to get them out. For once, I allow myself part of a prayer, without judgement. I direct it inwards towards myself, for myself. For in the very centre of my heart is hatred, injury, doubt, despair, darkness and sadness. Besides, it's from my favourite, Saint Francis: '...*Where there is hatred, let me sow love; Where there is injury, pardon; Where there is doubt, faith; Where there is despair, hope; Where there is darkness, light; Where there is sadness, joy...*'

That night I climb into Tennis John's bed and ask him to hold me tight. His gentle strength is what I seek. John must be the most nonviolent person I've met and yet one of the strongest men I've ever known. He knows who he is, and is content with himself. He whispers his thanks for allowing me to let him love me so honestly. In the security of his warm strong arms I tell him what happened, and his arms close even tighter around my shaking shoulders. He asks not one question, but tells me that he admires my strength to talk about it, to deal with it, to free myself of it. I tell him that despite my absolute loathing for violence, I feel so much hate for the man, that I could kill him.

'My dear boy, you at least know what it is that you feel and why you feel it, he most certainly does not. You can at least identify your potential to be violent and in so doing you are *not*. People like him are likely to deny that they are violent, so when they are, they are out of control. My dear boy, you are the stronger for you will arrive at a decision about what you do about it on an honest, open, conscious level; having worked things through in your heart and head. He can only react subconsciously and will remain a consumer of his own violence. You need do nothing to aid his destruction for he is, like all men of violence, in effect, destroying himself every time he acts.'

Drifting into sleep, I'm not sure that in telling John of the rape experience, I've simply not been seeking an easy alliance with a willing conspirator. Why can't I just accept things on face value? Why do I doubt people so much? As sleep comes, I decide not to tell either Joker or Angel, for I don't want an easy alliance, I want their friendship.

Slipping easily into the safety of dreamworld I become not a pop star or a war hero, but a bird, flying over ground-held cats. I am the most beautiful, the most majestic of birds. I ride the wind, circling the hungry cats. I dip my wings and glide with speed, over their heads, over their greed. I transcend their world, for I am above it. I ride the hot air of their world and transform it to suit the miracle of flight. My triumph is my flight, and my flight is all the power I need. I make patterns of celebration over the cats, then land, high on cliff tops, beyond their reach. I am content. I fold my wings across my back, knowing that in one singl movement I can be airborne again. No cat can live where I live, for here the bird is king.

Feeling sorry for myself serves only to weaken me, it has no other use. I've never seen a bird feel sorry for itself, even when caught by the cat, it fights the fight and dies like that. So with break of dawn, I rise and prepare a breakfast for John, which I serve to him in bed, with his morning mail. His delight is shown in his smile, and that same smile is reward enough for the boy who, in his dreams, has discovered that, once again, he is a bird.

Soldier Blue

In the morning mail there's a letter for me. It's from Joseph, my rib poking soldier, inviting me to spend a weekend with him. He has, he explains, a small flat which he keeps not far from his base in Farnborough, and I'm welcome to use it. He wants me to telephone him any evening after six. How can I go? I can't. I'd like to but... My thoughts are broken by the door bell. John opens the door and greets Banker with the same warmth he greets everyone. When John goes off to make coffee, I thank him for having introduced me to such a good man.

'And Banker, what about Joker and Angel? Do you know where they are?' I asked, scared to know the answer.

'Don't worry about them, they've gone with Biker, down to his sister's place in Cornwall.' He said, searching through his pockets.

'Are they okay?'

'They're fine. Joker did a wealthy punter and they've got plenty of cash...' He replied, pulling something from his jacket pocket.

'No, I don't mean are they okay for cash. I mean are they okay about having had to move from Actor's place?'

'You mean are they pissed off with you? No! Joker told me to give you this. He said you'd be worried.'

I opened the envelope as carefully and as slowly as I could, fearing the worst, and wanting the best. Inside was their address in Islington and a note which reassured me that all was well between us:

Dear Poet,

We've not been able to find you. Where the sodding hell you been? We have a great place in Islington and we have a room reserved for you when we get back. We've gone with Biker to see his sister. He's worried about her. Something to do with a fella or something. Angel wants to know if you've had any fresh cream dip lately? I don't know when we'll be back but you can move in anytime, okay. Just mention my name to the girl there. Her name is Slender, she's expecting you. She's sound. We miss you Poet.

Love, Joker, Angel & Biker.

When John came back into the room with a tray of coffee and put it down on the table by the sofa, I grabbed him and danced him around the room. He laughed and without a second thought, joined in my celebration, calling to Banker to put some music on. We fell about the place with joy but continued to dance to the music which Banker had selected. He put on the first thing which came to hand. It was the Toreador's Song, *Votre Toast* from Bizet's opera *Carmen*. I shall never forget it till the day I die. John sang. Banker joined in. It was one of those explosively beautiful moments when all differences and problems are banished through self abandonment. A moment never to be lost. I grabbed the moment and danced for all I was worth. Afterwards, I thanked Banker for bringing me the note and told him from now on I'd always think of him as being 'The Good Messenger' and the person who introduced me to opera. That evening I telephoned Joseph and told him that I'd be arriving the following weekend.

John insisted on me using one of his suitcases and buying me some new clothes. He saw me off at the station and told me to have a good time. Joseph was waiting for me at the other end, which made me feel wanted. He was dressed in casual civilian clothes and I barely recognised him. He looked so handsome and tall. The moment he saw me he rushed towards me and threw his arms around my shoulders.

'Here, let me take that.' He said, taking the suitcase.

'How are you, Joseph?' I asked, not quite sure how to talk to him.

'All the better for seeing you, Scouse.' He grinned, and punched me on the shoulder.

I guess I blushed, for he winked at me and laughed his friendly laugh as we headed towards the exit. Suddenly, I stopped, horrified. There, not two paces away from me, was an army officer. Joseph stopped, looked at me and then at the officer, then back at me.

'You know him?'

'Yes, and he knows me.' I replied, remembering his threat to thrash me within an inch of my life if ever I tried to see Alexander again.

'How?'

'He's someone who doesn't understand poetry.'

'What?' said Joseph, utterly confused.

'Nothing, I'll explain later. I've got to follow him.' I said and started to do just that.

'Scouse, what's going on? Why have you got to follow him? Who is he to you?' saiid Joseph, grabbing my arm.

'Joseph please help me. I have to find out where he lives. I'll tell you all about it later. But, now I have to follow him.'

'Tell me now. I'll help you, of course, just tell me...'

'He's the father of a... friend of mine and he doesn't want me to see him again. Joseph, I have to see him, do you understand?'

'A special friend?'

'A very special friend, and I don't know where to find him. I have to follow him...' I confided, pulling my arm free from Joseph's hand.

'Look, calm yourself, you don't have to follow him...'

'...I thought you understood...' I cried.

'...I do understand. I know who he is!'

'You know? What? Tell me! Joseph...'

'...You don't have to follow him. Calm down. He's a major in our mob, the same regiment, my mate's his batman. I know where he lives. He's got a tasty wife, two kids, a boy about your age and a girl about ten. They've got a dog...'

'Yes, that's them. Is it far?' I pleaded to know.

'It's minutes away from my place. So, let's get you there so we can leave your suitcase and give you time to get your head together. While you're doing that I'll nip over to my mate's and get your friend's telephone number, okay?'

'Joseph, I think you're wondeful. You must think I'm some kind of nutcase or something.'

He looked at for me for what seemed an age then he spoke quite sofly, his eyes never shifting from mine, and touching my soul;

'I don't think anything of the kind. I just recognise the signs, I know what you're going through, that's all.'

'Joseph, you know he's special, my friend?'

'Yes, I know, don't worry. But so are you, you know?'

'Joseph.' It was all I could say. I knew he felt for me the way that I felt for Alexander and yet here he was helping me to find the very person who could prevent anything developing between us. Before I could say another word he poked me in the ribs;

'Come on, lover-boy.'

I couldn't leave it just like that so I said, "Hang on a minute, we've got plenty of time, right? So how about you listen for a minute, okay? Look, my friend Alexander is special, very special.

71

But Joseph, that shouldn't get in the way of our friendship. I mean every friendship should be special, right? So how about a big hug, right now?"

He dropped the bag and flung his arms around me and I responded by throwing my arms around his waist and giving him a kiss on the cheek. What the hell, I didn't care what anyone thought. I liked Joseph very much and I wanted him to know that I did. Without looking around to see if anyone was looking, he daringly returned the kiss and told me that I was something special.

When we finally let our eyes wander from each other, we were confronted by a group of tutting old ladies in large hats, looking at us very disapprovingly over the tops of their glasses. I instantly gave Joseph another kiss for their benefit while they tutted even louder. It's crazy right? I mean, when a boy is not supposed to kiss another male in public? I've always hated rules and regulations, especially social rules which serve to keep things just the way they've always been. I instantly want to break a rule the moment it's pointed out. I don't mean rules like 'Thou shalt not kill', but daft stupid ones like 'Thou shalt be like everyone else', if you know what I mean. You know, those conforming rules?

The rule that demands that I be something I'm not is plainly stupid. If the fashion is short hair I grow mine long because I want to be me, not everyone else. You see, I detest conformity above everything else. And have you noticed all the signs in public places, places where kids hang around? They all begin with the words, 'Do Not...' Do not walk on the grass; do not play ball games here. Know what I mean? But there are just too many signs and besides the worst signs are never actually put up. You're supposed to know the rule. Like the sign which says 'Thou shalt not have sex with your own sex'.

While Joseph went off to his mates to get Alexander's telephone number I had a bath in the tiny bathroom, which Joseph had painted completely white. Unpacking John's suitcase, I saw that he'd placed five one pound notes inside one of the shirts. I sent him a silent thank you. The bedroom was delicately furnished. On the window shelf was a vase full of fresh cut flowers. The large double brass bed was covered in a hand made patchwork quilt of delicate pastel shades. Not what one would expect from a man in the Army. On the walls, in simple plain wooden frames, were pencil line drawings of half colthed young men, quite beautiful.

The room had the smell of polish, fresh furniture polish. A kind of peace filled the room and me. I could be at home here. When Joseph returned I was sitting in the small lounge with a pot of tea ready.

'You look as though you belong here,' he said, as though seeing through me.

'You've made it so lovely, Joseph, how could a person not feel at home?'

'I can be myself here. But with six months' rent already paid, we're being posted abroad. I'll give you a key, you can use the place anytime.'

I thanked him for the offer but what I actually wanted to hear was Alexander's telephone number.

'Where are you being sent?' I asked as sincerely as I could.

'Not sure, far east I think, but it could be anywhere. Why don't you call your friend while I put us a snack together?' He said, handing me a piece of paper with Alexander's address and telephone number on.

'I'll call him later. The important thing,' I said, following Joseph into the kitchen, 'is I've got his number. Joseph, I thought I'd lost him. I sent him a poem which his father got hold of because they've got the same name, there was no end of trouble about it. I didn't dare to try to contact him and then when I did I was told they'd moved and that they'd only rented the house for a couple of weeks. I met him on the same train I met you.

'You've found him now and I'm glad for you, honest Scouse, I'm really pleased. I hope he knows just how lucky he is? Remember, use this place when I'm gone, I'd hate the rent to be wasted.'

'We've only talked twice. The first time on the train and the second time in the park, while his sister was with us.'

'So you've not been alone with him?'

'No, more's the pity.'

'Then your wish shall come true my little freind. You can invite him here.'

'Here, but...'

'But nothing, I'm going to spend the evening with some of my mates. Call him, invite him over.'

'But...' I protested, 'what about us?'

'We have all day tomorrow for us. Call him.'

We ate the snack and Joseph listened to all my nervous talk of

73

Alexander. The tenderness of this big strong soldier was something to behold. His Welsh accent being music to the ears. Most people speak, and badly at that. The Welsh and the Geordies sing! What joy. Next time you get a chance listen to a Taff or a Geordie. Listen to the natural vowel sounds go up and down the register, magic! I listened to Joseph, spellbound, as he told me how he joined the Army as a boy soldier, how he was paid to swim, run and have fun with thousands of beautiful young men. He made it all sound so wonderful. The more excited he became the higher up the register went his voice. I decided it would be unwise to point out that being a soldier means taking orders, conforming, being prepared to kill and making violence an acceptable human attribute. Instead I asked him about his friends and what he did with them.

'Now that would be telling, young Scouse.'

So he *did* have a sexual outlet. I'd never given it much thought, had no need really, but all those men together, well, they must obviously have a fair amount of men who like sex with other men, right?

'Your set of keys are on the hook in the kitchen, they're yours, keep them. See you after eleven, okay?'

'Okay soldier boy, see you later and, by the way Joseph, thanks.'

'Forget it. See you later, have fun.'

Then he was gone. Alone, I couldn't force myself to pick up the telephone, so I washed the dishes and tidied up for a while. Then I smoked, then I tidied up again, then I had a wash, then I smoked another cigarette, then I cleaned my teeth. What was I afraid of? Of rejection, I think. What if he didn't want to see me? That was daft. I mean, I feared that before and he was delighted to see me. But now, well, perhaps his father has said something to him. Still unable to pick up the damn telephone I took out my notebook and wrote:

Soldier Blue

Stand easy, soldier blue,
Order arms, gangster crew.
Loving sons who play with guns, their
Duty obey, turn hairs to grey.
Incest armies that fuck each other,

Enlists the boy to cook his brother.
Robots one and robots all,
Become the boys who obey the call.
Losing in their victory, and Using up youths' ecstasy.
Every army kills liberty.

I find that as I close my notebook I'm crying such tears. I find myself grieving for the next soldier to be killed, wherever. The pain engulfs me and anger fills me at the sheer stupidity of the human race. How we fool ourselves into the belief that to kill a life can somehow be right. Don't get me wrong, if someone tried to kill me, I know that I could kill in order to defend myself. But I ask myself, how much killing is really justified? Idealistic and emotional nonsense? Perhaps. Perhaps not.

Softly Awakes My Heart

With all the courage I can muster, I dial the number. A woman answers. I freeze.

'Hello?'

Get a grip on yourself, answer her!

'Hello' I say, my voice cracking, 'may I speak to Alexander?'

'Yes, hold on. Who shall I say is calling?'

What shall I say? I daren't say Scouse. I nearly say Poet. Come on, think.

'Mark, Mark Crosbie.' I blurt, using my old street name.

Hold on, I'll get him for you.'

When the phone is put down on its side at the other end of the line, I'm tempted to hang up. I nearly do. What is he to think of someone called Mark Crosbie calling him?

'Hello, who is this?'

'Alexander, it's me, Scouse...'

'I say, really? Scouse? How on earth did you find me. I thought I'd never hear from you again. I waited for my poem...'

'...Oh, it's so good to hear your voice again. Look, I'll explain everything later, can you get away?'

'Yes, but where are you?'

'Here, here in Farnborough. I have the loan of a flat. Look it's all too complicated. Do you want to come over? I only have it for the evening.'

'Yes, yes, of course, I want to see you. Do you have my poem? Oh, just give me the address, quickly. Too many people here to talk freely.'

When I give him the address he tells me that he'll be here in less than twenty minutes. Then he hangs up. The tingling sensation running up and down my spine reminds me of the feeling I had when our lips met briefly on the train.

I have only just completed writing out his poems when he arrives at the door, out of breath. His breathtaking beauty is all I remember it to be. His dark hair shines as though filled with light. His hazel pupils set perfectly against the brilliant white of his eyes. His young face, full of pulsing colour breaks into a smile, and his pure white teeth show their glistening perfection. He is radiant. All we can do is look at each other, him in the hallway and me in the flat, holding open the door. I too break into a smile. We stand there, beaming at each other, as though this itself was enough. As though this itself was the climax of our friendship. The mutual unity of our spontaneous laughter allows me to step aside and for him to enter.

With the door closed we embrace and kiss. His lips are as soft and gentle as a dew covered flower petal on a spring morning. He tastes heavenly, young, fresh and very much alive. Our arms and hands explore each other's faces and the smoothness of his hands on my cheeks sends messages of tactile bliss to the very centre of my being. As he softly awakes my heart, I know that I love him. This moment, though I could never have imagined it, is the moment I have waited all my life for. I know this for I would die to preserve it. If something is worth living then surely it is worth dying for? He moves his head back and with arms around each other's waists we just look at each other. No thought is required here, for natural youthful instincts tell us to begin tentatively kissing the other, on the lips, on the face, on the eyes, on the neck. My hands, obeying the moment, go under his open jacket and slide up his firm chest, over his shoulders, down his arms, until the jacket slips easily from him. As one, we begin to undo the buttons of each other's shirts, starting at the top. With four buttons undone, he leans forward and kisses my exposed chest. Then, sensing my delight, he starts to lick my skin, around the nipples. Running my fingers through his hair I ask him to do it again. He does so and I hear him say, 'Your skin is so smooth'. Gently, I place my hand on his chin and lift his head, so that I can kiss the lips which have kissed me. Such round full voluptuous lips which only a boy can have. We embrace, locked into each other's tightly held arms. I could explode with happiness for he has the power to make me sing, he is a flower and he is king. He is pure and he is young, he is more than must be sung. He's the boy with hazel eyes, he's the joy and he's the prize. Taking his hand I lead him to the bedroom where I say, very softly,

'I want so very much to see you completely naked.'

'And I, you.'

With eyes fixed to each other we first, in perfect harmony, remove our shirts. His hairless olive skinned torso is perfectly formed for one so young. Strong firm shoulders and chest sit evenly on his narrow waist. His stomach, so flat and solid, seems as though carved in muscled ridges. I cannot believe this is happening, that such a beautiful boy is removing his clothes within arms reach of me. It's never been like this before, never. With shoes and socks kicked to one side, our hands move to each other's trousers. Our faces come together and I kiss him on and around his neck. Zips are tugged down and trousers fall unaided to the floor. Stepping from them we press our hips into each other. Through the remaining fine white material I feel his erect and pulsing boyhood press against my own. He stands back, his eyes penetrating right through mine into my soul, and then, putting his fingers into the top of his underpants, he waits for me to do the same, then, with one slow unified movement downwards, they're off.

At last, we are stark naked, fully erect and proud. What joy. This time it is he who takes my hand and leads me towards the huge bed. Climbing beneath the crisp sheets I feel his warm flesh on mine as we lay facing each other, hands exploring the other's smooth skin. There is no plan to what we do. We don't ask with words what pleases the other, instead we explore and listen to the language of our bodies. It is all the language we need, and more. It tells me that he likes me licking his chest, his flat hairless belly, his thighs. I know he enjoys it when I run my fingers through the springy black bushy hairs over his pulsing erection, for his hips lift up to meet my lips and hands. I know now what he wants. Starting on the inside of his smooth thighs I begin to lick and kiss my way up to his firm balls, over them, and then up the full length of his cock. I linger there, licking, kissing gently. His hips move upwards each time I near the proud full red knob, so that, now fully fluent in the language, I take him into my mouth, in the knowledge that we are in perfect harmony. I move my open eager lips up and down then pause and wait for him to move himself in and out. In and out. I complement the movement and join the motion. As he moves in so I move down his now hot and wet erection. His hands touching my neck and back tell me that he is near. A further movement tells me that he wants me to stop. As I let him go from my mouth he pulls me up and his lips press eagerly onto mine, his tongue darting in and out of my mouth. Slipping down my chest, my belly, he takes me directly into his warm mouth and I almost erupt instantly. He senses this and just holds me there, licking.

I lay flat on my back to give him space and his mouth begins to play with my erection. My head, ready to burst with joy, moves from left to right so that my cheeks almost slap the pillows either side. I touch his back and hearing the meaning he slips up my tight willing body until he is on top of me. Our erections slip and slide over the other and the moment is near. We move into each other's bellies, pulsing, lost to the moment. Then in perfect harmony we come, shooting up and up and up. Our bellies heave, our chests pound as we feel each other's cream merge into one glorified stream between us. We lay there for a good ten minutes, our erections spontaneously shooting out the last remaining cream. Even when it's all out our cocks seem unaware of the fact and jerk on. We lie in each other's arms and listen to the language going on between us. No words are needed as we fall gently into a restful, surface sleep.

I awake to feel him massaging my torso and thighs. I feel his lips brush against my neck. For a moment, as though still asleep, I lie there and enjoy the magic of this beautiful boy making love to me. My body, however, not hearing my head, responds and I reach out for him. Our love making begins again and I never want it to end, but it does and a couple of hours later we share a bath. We laugh and touch a lot. We wash each other all over and sing our heads off. He tells me he loves me.

Later, dressed again in the lounge, though without shoes or

socks, I tell Alexander all about his father arriving and the things he said. I explain how his father got hold of the poem instead of him, and I give the newly written version to him. I explain how I found him again and I tell him that I love him and don't ever want to be away from his side ever again. His sad eyes tell me that something is wrong. I silently beg him to tell me.

'Very soon we're off abroad, Singapore...'

'When? For how long?'

His beautiful eyes fill with tears as he speaks,

'It's hopeless isn't it. It's just not fair, we've only just found each other. But we shall always have this day, our day. It's soon, within a couple of weeks. It's a three year posting.'

I throw my arms around him and tell him that wherever he goes I'll find a way of getting to him.

'Just like I found you here,' though it flashes through my head by just how much chance I did so. 'I'll never let us be separated for long, never, I love you more than I can ever tell you.'

I believe my own words passionately but tears fill my eyes also as I see just how big the battle is. How on earth can a penniless rent boy of a poet get to Singapore. His silence tells me that he knows too that it's an impossible task. *Singapore boy, wing you away; sing, a poor boy, sing castaway*.

Afterwards, tears dried, I walk with Alexander as far as we dare to his home. I give him Tennis John's telephone number and address and tell him again that I'll find a way. I remind him that if for whatever reason I don't seem to be able to contact him or he is unable to contact me to pass a message through his father's batman. We sqeeze hands at the corner of the street and I watch him being swallowed up by the big front door of his house. I swear, on my life, that I will see him in Singapore, come hell or high water.

When Joseph arrived back with fish and chips we sat in the kitchen and ate them while I poured out the whole story of Alexander to him. He listened attentively and agreed to act as go-between with his mate the batman, should the need arise. He confessed that he had no idea just how much in love I actually was and that his love for me had become even stronger. Later, in bed, I shared sex with him, the way one does with a friend. It's not love making but unashamed sexual sharing at the most human level. It is none the less for all that. We had a good time and slept comfortably afterwards. He was indeed a friend worth caring for.

On my way back to London I wrote to Joseph thanking him for all he was and for all he'd done for me. Then I felt urged to write about Alexander. What ended up in the notebook was not one single word, for there are some things just too great for words to capture. They are what they are, beautiful moments and they should be felt as that, left at that. What I felt was that I'd shared an experience with another boy which held me enchanted, for in that experience I *was* love, he *was* love. How rare to touch. I was left with a great pain that I'd never set eyes upon him ever again. How can such a love not be able to dare speak its name? How can such a love be thought of as less than any other love? When we told each other that we loved the other, we were simply using words to find a way of saying what we knew to be a great reality. It was beyond construction, beyond making up. For the first time in my life I came to believe that I knew what being 'in' love meant. It means that I am love, that he is love, that together we are love, that what we do is love, that what we want for the other is love.

I discovered, too, that love enhances love because it is selfless. I also know that I can never be the same again. I know that somehow, despite its inherent addictve nature, I have to get of the rent scene. I've got to take Joker's advice and empty my jug of everything which isn't self selected goodness. I've got to love through a new kind of living, and not live through a paid kind of loving. My whole body is excited at this mind blowing discovery that I can take charge of my life. But deep within that damn jug of mine is a voice which calls out, telling me that I feel this way because I've just had good sex with a beautiful boy. It's a lie! Isn't it?

Brixton Billy

Tennis John listens as I explain about Alexander's going abroad. As always he is supportive. He passes no judgements but instead tells me that I should do what I feel to be right and that, whatever it is, I have his support. But I don't know what to do. All I know is that the boy I love is going abroad, for three years.

After a couple of days of moping around John's flat I decide it's time I pull myself together and get some air. I miss my friends and need to see Joker, Angel and Biker. It really is strange how absence has the effect of throwing a spotlight on the quality of friendship, only then does one see its true nature.

In a similar kind of way, I seem to understand more now about my father and my Liverpool culture, than ever I did when closer to both. With the time and space now between me and my father in Liverpool, I seem more tolerant and forgiving. Even the sound of the place in my head, *Liverpool*, takes on a new warmth, a new meaning. It's as though, somewhere in my heart, I have endowed the place with qualities not visible or accessible in the place itself. Perhaps the passionate qualities I give the place are only accessible from afar or from within my own imagination.

Like a homing pigeon, I make my way to the Dilly and The Meat Rack, and decide to hang around for a while to see if Joker and the others show their faces. If they don't I'll try going to their squat and meeting the girl Joker mentioned in his note. What was her name? I know it was strange. Got it, Slender! But I guess it's no stranger than Poet, really. I bet Joker gave her the name. Being on The Meat Rack again brings me into a kind of spiritual union with my friends, so I let that feeling become the centre, effectively pushing away the memory of the sordid rape. I allow myself just one thought about that, the man must have been as sick as someone with cancer!

Lighting a cigarette, I turn my attention to watching out for friends and try to find a suitable phrase to say to them when we meet, but they all sound corny in my head, so I disregard them in favour of throwing my arms around them. Touch, I figure, is worth a thousand words. Just as I'm about to throw away the cigarette butt, a kid of about thirteen comes up to me and asks me for it. I look at him. He looks cocky and streetwise. I flick the butt away and offer him a full cigarette. Taking it, he asks me if there are any good punters about. I can't help but see myself in the kid, just two or three years previously. I tell him I'm waiting for some friends and have not really been taking too much notice of punters.

'I did a good'un the other night. Twenty quid and all I had to do was jack him off, twenty quid.'

To toss him off? Twenty quid? Get away, straight?' I said, playing the kid along.

How many times have I heard myself and other rent boys tell that lie? Too many.

'Yea, He goes, "I'll give you twenty quid." So I goes, "Okay!" He was the manager or something of some geezer in the films, you know

81

the one in all them films, the one who's on the cover of that magazine, you know?'

I mention the names of some film stars and the kid says, 'Yea, that's him.'

I don't ask him which one. I don't want to force the kid into making up more than he can handle. So, I ask him his name and where he's from. His lovely black face tells me that he's not from Mayfair.

'Billy, from Brixton! What's yours?'

'Poet, from Liverpool.'

'You a poet then?'

'Kind of.'

'Go on, straight? Say one then.' He asks disbelieving.

I look at the kid and warm to his innocence and vulnerability. I guess what I see in there is the same as what Joseph saw in me. He looks confident and streetwise but very exploitable.

'I can't just say one like that.' I explain, smiling.

'You 'aint no *poet* then, are yer?'

'I guess not.'

'Go on say one.'

'But you said I wasn't a poet, you said so yourself.'

'Say one, go 'ed.'

'I'll have to make one up.'

'What, just like that?'

'It's called a limerick.'

'Is that a poem?'

'Kind of. It's a kind of Irish poem, a fun poem.'

'You Irish then?'

'No English, just like you. Do you want to hear it or not?'

'Yea, go on. I was born here, you know.'

'I figured that, so was I.'

'My parents come from overseas.'

'So do mine.'

'But you're white.'

'So?'

'Which part of overseas?'

'Ireland.'

'That's not overseas. I mean places like Jamaica, that's overseas.'

'I guess you're right, I never thought of it like that.' I concede.

'Say that thing, then.'

'The limerick?'

'Go on then.'

'Okay, but remember, I've got to make it up as I go along, okay?'

'Yea, you said that, go on do one about me.'

'About you?'

'Yea, you're a poet 'aint yer?'

'I think you're the poet.'

'Don't mess about, I'm still at school. Say it then, go on.'

'*A young lad from Brixton once said...*'

'That's me, right?'

'I haven't finished yet, can I go on?'

'Yea, go on.' He giggles.

> *'A young lad from Brixton once said,*
> *I wish I'd stayed home in bed,*
> *Than around with the lags,*
> *Just bumming their fags,*
> *So he went back to school instead.'*

That it? You must be joking! School? No chance! What's a *lag* then?'

'It's what you'll turn into if you hang around places like this, a villain, a thief, a rogue.'

'You a lag, then? You don't look like a lag, just on the game, right?'

'Never mind that, did you like the limerick?'

'Was alright I suppose. But you're on the game, right?'

'Right and thanks for nothing.' I say, acting cut up.

'Well it's obvious 'aint it and anyway you asked me didn't yer? What's your name then?'

'I told you, Poet.'

'No, I mean yer real name?'

'How long you been on the game Billy?'

'Long enough.'

'Long enough to know that you never ask another rent boy his name?'

'I know that. I was just testing that's all.'

'Sure you were.'

'I was, and Billy's not my real name anyway.'

'Oh yea.' I say, entering the spirit.

'Yea, I hate my real name 'cos it's the same as my dad's. So I never use it, see!'

'Good for you. So what's your dad's name then?'

The same as mine, soft arse. You don't catch me out like that, see. See you round, like a doughnut.'

'You're a smart kid.' I say, offering another smoke.

'Yea, I know Poet, I know, see?' He laughs, indicating that he's about to go.

'I see. You look after yourself Billy, you hear.'

'Don't worry about me I'm cool, know what I mean.'

Then he was gone, lost in the crowds, taking with him his innocence and poetry, along with yet another of my cigarettes. I shake my head in amazement at the kid's streetwise confidence and his attractive yet terrifying vulnerability.

Billy is the new kind of rent boy and, coincidentally, also the first black rent boy I've met. He lives at home and does the business without anyone knowing. He dips into the scene and out of it at his leisure. The Billys' of this world don't run away but lead a double life. A good number of boys who like sex with other boys and men adopt a similar double life style. These are the ones in search of a good sexual experience, who somehow give out the non-verbal message that they are on the rent scene. So, when they score, when a man approaches and offers money, they may be surprised but they may also ask for money next time around. You see, the non-verbal message a true rent boy gives are very similar to the ones a boy gives out when he is on the look out for a same sex adventure. It becomes part of the buzz, part of the game. But it's a different game to the one Joker, Angel, Biker and I are on. We are on the survival game, while they are on a kind of pleasure or hedonistic trip.

Adults, that is parents, don't like to think of their adolescent kids as being sexual, let alone same-sexual. So, when a teenage boy wants to explore a same sex experience he often turns to a rent boy because he knows where to look. It's true more often than folks want to believe. It's a strange encounter to be picked up by a punter near your own age. I mean, imagine it, a good looking boy, who could have anyone he wants, pays another boy to have sex with him. I've even had punters younger than me and remember I'm only fifteen, and they're not all rich kids either. Some pay just to see if they'll like it, others to test out their sexual orientation in a kind of non-threatening way. You know, try it with a rent boy who you never have to see again and who knows nothing about you. While others, like many adult punters, pay in order to feel more in control of the situation. They lack confidence and couldn't get it up unless they felt themselves to be in charge of what was going on.

You know I was telling you earlier how I just kind of melt into the arms of a kind caring type of punter, especially when he tells me that I'm beautiful or whatever, well, these punters melt in the same kind of way when you tell them that they are really sexy.

The Best of Plans

Lost in my thoughts of the rent scene I fail to see or even hear the figure creep up behind me. I nearly jump out of my skin when hands are clasped around my eyes and a voice, a voice I instantly recognise, begins to speak in familiar Winston Churchill tones:

'When a friend comes back into your life and he is pleased to see you, then there can be no uncertainty about the quality of his friendship. Know this, young Poet, I am pleased to see you, and you, unable to control your joy are delighted to see me, are you not? Speak, you may speak!'

I didn't want to speak, I just wanted to hear his voice and feel his hands on my face but he spun me around bringing us face to face. All I could do was to burst out laughing, so filled with relief to see him, then I said;

'I've missed you, and your sayings. I've really missed you. How's Angel? Is he okay? And Biker, is he okay? You know damn well that I'm delighted to see you.'

We exchanged touches and smiles which made smiles. 'Biker's still at his sister's and Angel should, at this very moment,' he said, looking at his watch, 'be climbing back into his clothes, somewhere in Knightsbridge. The new flat will blow your mind and so will Slender. She's an American and describes herself as a fat fag hag. I think it's just that she likes rent boys, anyway she owns the flat, well, rents it anyway, and she must weigh about fifteen stone or more. That's why we call her Slender. And to answer your next question, no it's not a squat. We told that to Actor and the others to keep him and his cronies away. You know, the brothers grim? It's a great set up and we can even do business from there, no hassle. The only thing missing is you, where the soddin' hell have you been?'

'I've missed you so much Joker, I can't tell you. Let me take you for a meal or something and we can talk there. Are you hungry?'

'Are you kidding or what? Lead on MacDuff.'

After a meal we ended up in the Two 'I's' coffee bar and I told Joker everything which had happened since I last saw him. I even told him about the rape. I was with a friend and everything just poured out naturally and without censorship. Joker asked me to describe the guy as best as I could so that he could put the word about. My descriptions were shadowy and disjointed but as Joker pumped me for detail, a picture began to emerge of the man and his car. Having focused on the car and its internal layout, Joker figured it was a Ford Consul or Zephyr. The colour being either blue or black. It was surprising just how much I could recall with the help of my friend. At the end of the coffee we had a pretty fair idea of the man to look out for.

By the end of the third frothy coffee Joker understood about the depth of my love for Alexander and of my need to get to Singapore.

'What you need, then, is to get as much bread as you can, as fast as you can, right?'

'Right!'

'So what you have to do is get yourself organised, right?'

'Right!'

'Well, you can do that the minute you move in with us. I mean, the punters can come to us. We can get something really good going, you me and Angel. We could have our own little set up. We could make a fortune, right?'

'You mean open a brothel?'

'A house of pleasure, for tired businessmen. Don't use tatty words like brothel, please, it lowers the tone.'

'Could we really make a lot of money, quickly?'

'You bet your sweet wee arse!'

'Enough to get me to Singapore?'

'Why not?'

'Then you're on. Let's go for it.' I agreed. 'But I can't move in right away though.'

'Why not?'

'It's Tennis John, he's okay, I can't just walk out, he's been really decent, you know?'

'So when?'

'Give me a week, I owe him that, okay?'

'Take as long as you want Poet, John's sound. But take these, they may come in handy.'

Joker handed me some papers.

'What's this?'

'A new identity, in case you get pulled. You can thank Biker for them, he's taken a shine to you.'

Looking through the papers I had a driving licence, a birth certificate and a bunch of letters addressed to a person called Edward Larkin, aged eighteen. Joker told me to subject the lot to memory, especially the date of birth and the address, which was Manchester, and to always keep them on me, just in case.

'And, if you get pulled, don't forget to talk like you come from Manchester, and get rid of anything with your real name on.' Seeing my concern, he continued, 'Don't worry, they're not hot, Biker got them off a mate of his, he's sound.'

'What about you?'

'I've got my own, had them for ages. All organised rent boys have false identity papers, and Angel and I are organised. How do think we've got by without Lilly law picking us up? And remember, we're going to make a fortune, working together. Talking about work, there's only two reasons for working Poet, one, because you're doing with your life what it is you really want to do or two, to get the money so that you can do what it is you really want to do. And that's what you're going to do, right? You're going to Singapore, right?'

'Damn right!' I agree, throwing my arms around him.

'Take it easy, Poet, gratitude is sometimes the obligation felt by those who are unsure of their friends or by those who can't see the catch when they receive a gift from a punter. Biker likes you, it's as simple as that. He doesn't want to see you get caught. He said something about how you covered him up in bed one morning.'

'He was freezing and looked so scared of things. I just put his blankets back over him, that's all. Though I nearly kissed him on the forehead.'

'And the other blankets, from the other bed!'

'That's right but how did he know it was me? He was fast asleep.'

'He asked us, when we all got up and as it wasn't us, it must have been you, easy. He said it was the first time he'd ever woken up

87

feeling warm and that you made terrific toast soldiers. That's Biker for you.'

'He's really fragile, isn't he?'

'We all are Poet, but I know what you mean. He puts on a great show of being the hard case, but he's just a scared kid, like the rest of us. His kind of fear lives real close to the surface though, you can see him tasting it with every breath. He doesn't say much but once, when he was a bit pissed, I heard him say to this other kid, on the Dilly, he said, and he really meant it, he said, "I'm scared of no one, no matter how big or tough he is, but I'm terrified of myself." The kid asked him what he meant so he goes, "I can fight the bastards when I can get hold of them but in your head you can't get hold of them." The kid backed off, like most of us would and Biker just laughed.'

I left Joker at the Dilly and a week later, and after much soul searching about leaving Tennis John's, I moved into the new flat. Tennis John told me that I always had a room whenever and if ever I needed one. I didn't think it right to tell him of my plans though I did tell him that I just had to get to Singapore, and I didn't much care how I managed it. I think he understood.

To make me welcome, Slender cooked us all a great feast of a meal. Later, Angel came into my room, when the flat was all bedded down, carrying a pot of fresh cream. It was his way of saying welcome home, so we dipped most of the night and fell asleep in each other's arms. I felt wonderfully at home.

Over the following months we had our house of pleasure well organised. We paid Banker a percentage for every boy loving punter he introduced and we paid Slender a similar amount, to look after us. We did individual punters in our own rooms or Angel and I worked in pairs, putting on shows for the richer boy-lovers. Occasionally, we arranged an orgy scene for those with money to burn. When Biker returned from his sister's he would do those punters who liked to get spanked and things, or he would perform with his girlfriend for those who just wanted to look. The money was rolling in and we left it safely in Slender's safe keeping. The punters would arrive, we would do whatever it was they wanted, they would leave contented and we would prepare for the next one, equally contented.

A few of the punters we recognised from the newspapers or the television but we never made comment. They had a right, the same as everyone else. There's no doubt that if all the rent boys and rent girls exposed all the punters they've ever done, then the world of politics, amongst others, would be reshaped. But exposing others was not, and is not, for me to do. I'll leave that to those with pure white souls.

So, without caring very much about who the punters were, we did our very best to satisfy their needs, providing they could pay the price, which was not negotiable, except upwards. We experimented with ways to please our guests, and we always treated them as such. Those with time we would massage with warm scented oils (Angel's idea). Those with little time, would be allowed to come as quickly as they wanted. Our philosophy was simple; a good profit and a quick return. That is, we aimed to get as much as we could and get the punter to want to come back again soon. We also worked hard at getting as much sexual pleasure as we could from whatever scene was constructed. The more we enjoyed, then the more the punter enjoyed it.

The one scene I always turned down, though, was if the punter wanted to tie me up. I simply couldn't get into it and I lost my erection when I tried it once for a regular. Most punters got what they wanted, however, with four boys and one girl to select from. Without doubt, the most popular talk the punters liked to hear was to be told about having sex with other boys at school. When the punter got real horny and his money became more easily given, we would then offer to share him with one of the other boys. Angel and I did the fresh cream dip routine so many times that we almost lost interest in it ourselves; variations kept us alive to its pleasures though.

Money ceased to be a problem and while the others spent theirs on clothes and stuff, I saved most of mine with Slender. She thought my plan to join Alexander 'just divine'. That was her favourite word, 'divine'. She also thought it 'divine' that I send small gifts to Tennis John for sending me Joseph's new address in Singapore.

Sometimes, I'd go out of my way to talk to the odd rent boy myself, especially if he looked down on his luck, and take him for a meal and slip him a few quid. I asked the others if they ever gave another rent boy money like this and was relieved to hear that they considered it, not only a perfectly normal thing to do, but also a kind of duty to spread the wealth around. Or as Joker put it,

'Who else is prepared to help a rent boy, without sooner or later wanting either his arse or his soul, or both?'

'I tell you now, Joker, one day I'm going to do something to help rent boys. Set up some kind of project or something.'

'Good on you Poet, but they'll crucify you if you try. I mean a rent boy helping other rent boys? No way!'

Missing Presumed...

When Angel didn't show up one night none of us became concerned, for each of us would occasionally take time off to do our own thing, without explanation. We sometimes needed space for ourselves. Angel was no exception, he would sometimes go on his own to do the odd punter. So did I. It was like a kind of addiction to the street scene. We needed to touch it just to make sure we were still in tune. It's not that we needed the money, it was more complicated than that. Boys like Angel and I had worked the streets for so long that it got in the blood, it became a part of you, and not to touch it once in a while was like not being with yourself.

It was only on the second day that we each began to voice our concern. Had he been picked up by the law? Was he being held, like I had been? Was he back in some far away kids home? None of us knew! All we could do was speculate. Biker became convinced that the law had him and that he was back in the kids home.

We began a search. We went to every place we knew he liked. We called up punters, we went to places he didn't like. Nothing! Not a damn thing. Biker, convinced as ever that he was back in the kids home, talked Joker into telephoning them. The truth of the matter was that Joker didn't require much persuading. He phoned his social worker who wanted him to give himself up, and return under his own steam to the home. Joker listened, frustrated, and eventually got a promise from him that he would check to see if Angel had been picked up. When Joker phoned hours later, at the pre-arranged time, his face told us that Angel was not with the police or in a kids home. Joker hung up and became even more anxious and depressed. Gone was the quick line in wit. I took my money from Slender and spread it around amongst Joker, Biker, his girl, Slender herself and kids on the street. Very quickly, I was flat broke and still no word from Angel.

We went off in different directions, returning to the flat at the end of the night with nothing but increased anxiety. Joker told us that he had tried to get the names and addresses from Banker, of all the punters he knew who were into young boys, but Banker wouldn't come across. Biker's solution was both instant and realistic, he and I would break into the Earl's Court flat the following day and take the address book.

We arrived in Earl's Court around midday and waited to see if there was any movement at the flat. Actor came out carrying his laundry. This should have given us about an hour. Checking to see if the key was in the usual place Biker cursed, it wasn't. He banged on the door, to see if anyone was in and when no one came he got to work. From inside his coat he produced a steel bar and within seconds, forced the door open. Going straight to Banker's bed, I found his address book almost too easily. It was sitting on top of a pile of books. Biker, worked up by the thrill of breaking in, was searching around the flat for, well your guess is as good as mine. He was all pumped up. Before I could even protest, he'd forced the locks on Actor's room and was in there like a ferret after a rabbit. He knew exactly what he wanted and went straight to the suitcases. Without concern or ceremony, he forced a lid open.

'Take a look at this lot Poet.' He said, amazed.

'Leave it out Biker, we've got what we came for, let's get out of here.'

'We've got loads of time, come on, I know you're just as curious as me, look for yourself.'

He was right of course, I looked over his shoulder and let my eyes fall upon the contents of the suitcase.

'What is it?' I asked, 'it looks like marzipan.'

'Explosives, I think. Plastic explosives!'

'Let go Biker, we're out of our league here.'

'In a minute,' he said, forcing open other cases.

'Detonators! Jesus H. Christ, Poet, it's a bleedin' arsenal. They've had us carrying around enough stuff to blow ten banks. Actor's punter? Did you ever meet him, or what?'

'No and I don't want to thank you very much! Let's get the hell out of here, please, Biker. I can't handle this.'

'He must be in with the brothers grim, right?'

'Biker! I don't give a monkey's toss who's in with who. Let's go. We've got what we came for. Biker! It's Angel we're interested in, not this bloody lot.'

'It's not as simple as that Poet! They'll know, he'll know, Actor. They'll know it was us lot who broke in.'

'In the name of God, *how*?'

'Come on Poet, who else would, ask yourself?'

'So what do we do? We don't have much time?'

'We torch the place and make it look like an accident.'

'The front door, we bust it open for God's sake. That won't look like an accident. For heaven's sake Biker, there might be people upstairs. Leave it! Just leave it and let's go!'

'They'll come after us!'

'Not if we leave things just as they are!'

'Don't be daft Poet! Look, we have to cover ourselves, right? I don't have to remind you what they do to people, do I?'

'Then why not just tip the police off?'

'What? Let them find this lot?'

'Why not? It would look like they knew what they were looking for?'

'I'm no grass, Poet!'

'Look, Biker, I just want to get out of here and find Angel and tipping off the police is a lot less dangerous than setting fire to the place. Do you really think Actor didn't know about this lot? Okay, let's just get out of here, let's just leave it, okay?'

'I say we torch the place!' he said, smashing the bar down on top of a box. 'They've had us carting this stuff around on the bleedin' tube for peanuts. They could've killed us.'

'I say we don't! Biker, please! You're just using this as an excuse. You're just thinking about being conned. It's obvious to anyone that you must have gone through hell in your life, most likely been conned a lot. You want to torch the goddamn world, for God's sake! What's gone is gone, let it go!'

'I'm thinking about us all being in one piece tomorrow!' He shouted, opening a box of matches.

'To some extent, okay, that's true. But don't do something which could kill innocent people, you'd regret it for the rest of your life. Look, it's going to take more courage just to walk away from this lot, and you know that! So, come on, I know you're no chicken. Let's just walk away. Damn it Biker, I wouldn't be talking like this if I didn't care about you. You know I care! You sent those identity papers with Joker because you were concerned about me. Well, now I'm concerned about you. Just trust me, just let me take care of you right now because you're not thinking straight. Let's get going now, okay?'

'That's not fair, Poet.'

'Just wipe the cases clean and let's go! Besides the explosion alone would probably bring the whole damn street down, look at how much stuff is here. Think about it, I'm going, with or without you.'

'You fight dirty Poet, way below the belt.'

'Only for those I care about Biker. Come on, let's go.'

With great relief to me, Biker put away his matches and followed me out of Actor's room and out of the flat. We left the door, as it was, wide open. As we walked towards the tube station I couldn't help thinking that it is better not to know some things. Knowledge means that some actions must follow and that we'll never be the same again. We knew now what Actor's great secret was, he was a storeman for the heavies of London. He was up to his eyes in it and given the links with Banker's punter, then Banker was probably just as involved himself. We were well out of it. It could very well be that we'd carried nothing more harmful than a load of porn around the underground, but on the other hand, well, who knows?

Banker's address book revealed only a couple of names and addresses which, between the rest of us, we didn't know. While Joker and I went to check one out, Biker went off with his girlfriend to check out the other. On the way, I put Joker in the picture about Actor's secret. It didn't seem to make much impression on him for he had become more and more depressed about Angel's absence. The punter turned out to be someone we knew under a different name and he said the last time he saw Angel was at our place. Biker's search was equally fruitless, with that punter being scared silly by what could happen to him, with all the fuss.

'There's only one thing for it Poet! We have to find that place in the East End where that bloke held you prisoner!' said Joker, that night. 'We'll tool up and search for the place tomorrow.'

Tooling up meant taking whatever weapons we could. So that's what we did. Biker with his bar. Joker with a hammer and me with a knife. With serious intent we headed for the East End and the docks. We walked and walked and the other two probed and encouraged me to remember, but it was hopeless. All the buildings looked the same to me. Near to giving up, some six hours later, Joker suddenly said;

'What about that, Poet?'

'Could be, I'm not sure. One car looks very much the same as another.'

'But this one's here Poet! What about the colour, it's blue! You said you thought the car was blue.'

Looking inside the car brought the memory of what happened to me flooding back. It was the car.

'This is it!'

'You sure about that?' asked Joker.

'If he says so, that's good enough for me,' hissed Biker.

'I'm sure, this is it,' I said, choking on the words.

Joker put his arm around my shoulders and quietly said,

'Take your time Poet. Which building is it? Take your time, don't rush, just look around and think back. You don't have to come in.'

'I want to! I'm coming! I want to meet him face to face! I'm not sure but it has to be unused, empty, windows blocked off. Like that one, right there!'

The building was an old warehouse, apparently empty. Quietly, we tested windows and doors until we found a loose cover on a broken window. Like mice we entered without a sound and stood in the dark, giving our eyes time to adjust. Like a television set just warming up, slowly, a picture began to emerge. Before us was a narrow corridor, at the end of which was a door standing ajar. My chest was heaving and my pulse beat out a sound, which in my own ears sounded like a drum. Half way along the corridor we froze when we heard a muffled voice. I knew that voice! It's him! I grabbed the knife from my belt and almost charged the open door. Biker grabbed me and pushed me firmly but gently up against the wall. I had internally lost all control. I wanted to kill and Biker recognised the signs. As Biker whispered to me so Joker stroked my face.

'Take it easy, he's going nowhere Poet. My turn to take care of you now, you'll get your shot. When we get through the door, spread out and come in on him from different angles and don't do anything until I give the signal, okay?'

Through the shadows we spread out as the vile man spoke his vile talk to the thrust up figure on the floor below him. This disgusting low life should be dead, and I'm just the one to do it. I saw, in my mind's eye, the knife plunge deep into the man's heart, ending his perverted existence for ever. If Biker didn't act soon then I was going to take the monster out all by myself. I could wait no longer, I dashed across the open space and heard Biker yell,

'Get the bastard!'

Biker's there first and lets his bar land heavily across the back of vermin. Then Joker lands his hammer on the vile disgusting low life's elbow. Low life screams and it's music to my ears. I want to hear him cry out for mercy before I kill him. I lunge at him, the knife aimed at his chest, and I trip over the figure below me. Landing next to him I see that it's Angel. He's lost in some drugged world and is obviously terrified at what's going on around him. To get over the noise of the fight, the blows and the curses, I have to scream at the top of my voice,

'It's Angel! It's Angel! It's Angel!'

The other two stop landing the blows on the now floored and unconscious vermin.

'Get some light in here,' I cry.

Biker rips away a window shutter and light floods in showing us the scene in broad daylight. Angel is thrust up in precisely the manner I had been and doesn't seem to recognise any of us. He nods his head repeatedly. I know what he's doing. He's staying alive, he's surviving. Biker searches through the vermin's belongings and finds the keys to release Angel.

'Let's get him cleaned up and dressed,' cries Joker, face wet with rage and tears, shaking all over.

I search the floor for the knife and when my hand lands on it I lunge at the vermin's chest. Biker's kick nearly breaks my wrist and the knife is sent hurtling in the air.

'He should die!' I scream.

'Could be,' says Biker picking up the knife and holding it out to me. 'No, you're right! He should die! Go on Poet *kill* him. Take the knife and *stab* him to *death*, go on. What are you waiting for. Do It! Kill the Bastard! What are you waiting for?' He shouts, plunging the knife into thin air.

In his rage, Biker shows me myself and I freeze in horror at the sight. I look from the drugged Angel, to Joker, to the blood covered vermin on the floor and back to Biker. Screaming, I burst into uncontrollable tears.

'He should die, he *should*.' I sob, looking at Angel in Joker's arms.

Biker, despite his sorrow, takes charge.

'Get Angel dressed Joker, come on I'll help. Poet, find the car keys and get the hammer and bar.

With Angel hanging between Joker and me, Biker chains the vermin to a post in the middle of the floor and throws the keys to the far side of the room. Then, taking all the time in the world he goes through the vermin's pockets and takes his money. Taking the knife he slashes all the clothes to pieces, then perfectly calmly he goes over the area wiping out footprints and any other traces.

'He'll come to in a couple of hours and will raise the alarm. He'll have a lot of explaining to do. He won't be wanting to touch another rent boy for a while. We'll get Angel home and then I'll dump the car way out, let's go.'

It was only later, in the car, with me nursing my aching wrist, that I realised how Biker had saved the day. I thanked him and he said that any of us would have done the same thing. He was generous to the extreme, for I doubt that I would have stopped him. The knowledge that I was no more than two feet away from killing sent me into shivers of fright. I knew then that I could kill another human being!

Joker and I sat on the back seat with our drugged up friend between us. Joker talked to Angel all the time, telling him it was all over and that he was safe, and we both stroked him. At one point Joker's eyes caught mine and he remarked that he now understood what I'd been through.

'The terrible thing,' I said to the back of the seat in front of me, 'is that I thought I'd kind of worked all the hate through, I thought I'd coped with what happened, I thought I had my violence under control, yet without you Biker, I'd have killed him. I grew up with violence and detested it, yet I could easily have been a killer!'

Biker looked at me through the driving mirror and said,

'Eh, after what you must have been through, and what Angel's been through, I mean, anyone would have reacted just like you did. Anyone! Right Joker?'

'You better believe it, Poet. But it's out now, it's out of you and you know you can deal with it.'

'Yea, Poet it's like you said to me, you know, you said it's gone so let it go, remember?'

'I know, but I'm as confused as anything. I mean, how can someone who hates violence want to kill? It's crazy,' I asked, not expecting an answer.

'That's it! You've got it!' said Biker, 'it's crazy! The whole thing was crazy, *is* crazy. And how can you expect to act sane in an insane situation? I mean, if you did, then that would really be crazy, right? It's not us that created the craziness, remember that, all we did was deal with it, the best way we could, and we did what we had to do, no more!'

'But it scares the shit out of me to know that I could kill!' I cried.

'All of us could kill, Poet, all of us. You're not alone in that,' said Biker, to the mirror. 'Create the right circumstances and even your grandmother could kill. You're lucky enough to have discovered the fact now, while you're just a kid.'

'He's right, Poet,' said Joker, taking my hand. 'And remember, words are absolutely useless when the enemy speaks a different language. Sure we used violence but we stopped before violence used us. There's a big difference.'

'I didn't want to stop, though. I wanted to hear him scream for mercy and I wanted him dead. I'll be straight with you, I still do.' Suddenly Biker pulled the car into the side of the road. 'Oh shit, look who's here.' He said, thumping the steering wheel.

Getting into the back of a car, a car none of us could fail to recognise, just outside our flat, were Actor and Banker. In the front seat was the boy fancier of the brothers grim. Alongside him was another tough looking man. Joker thought he was Actor's sugar daddy. None of them looked too happy. Once again, we let Biker take charge. He told Joker and me to wait in the car while he checked the coast was clear. Within a few minutes he was back.

'It's clear. You two take Angel in and I'll park the car around the corner, I've got a feeling we're going to need it.'

After giving Angel a bed bath we agreed that one of us should be with him until the drug wore off. None of us got much sleep and by the morning we knew we had to get the hell out of London for a while. All Slender could tell us was that some men called asking for us. That was good enough, they obviously knew who broke into the flat. When Angel awoke, we put him in the picture and he agreed we had to leave. Biker told Slender to tell the men the truth, when they called again. That we had left and she'd no idea where we'd gone. We kissed and hugged her and half an hour later we were heading north, out of London. Angel sat close to me and I put my arms around him. No words were needed. I just stroked him and let him be. He became, in my head and in my heart, all the rent boys who've ever been and who are ever likely to be. One day, one day, people will hear. When Angel began to cry, so did I, so did Joker, so too did the tough Biker. *One day, one day*.

Taking stock

W hen it became apparent that we had no place to go, I told Biker to head for Farnborough, and Joseph's flat. I still had the key and with rent already paid on the place it was the perfect bolt hole. At least, until we worked out where we went from there. I have to confess, though, that I held back mentioning the place as long as I could. Taking others, even if they were friends, to the place where Alexander and I made love felt very strange...

Pushing open the door and returning the key to my pocket I stepped over the small pile of letters on the floor and stopped in the doorway. Taking a deep breath. I could taste Alexander. I could see him taking off his white shirt... I could... I could feel his lips touching mine...'

'Come on Poet, show us around,' said Angel, breaking into my dream.

'This is it,' was all I could say, as the others went on in to the flat, 'this is the place. We should be safe here.'

Most of the letters were for Joseph but there was one with my name

on it. Just my name. It had obviously been hand delivered. I dropped
the others and ripped open the envelope,

My own dear Richie,

*I begged and pleaded with my parents to send me to school in England but
they insisted on me going with them. I feel so lost and empty knowing that
we are being torn apart. I really don't know if this letter will even reach
you. You are so elusive. So, I've sent a copy to the address you gave me,
the one in London, care of John. I don't even have a photograph of you.
I hope you don't think I look too silly in mine. I hate the school uniform,
but it's the only snap I could lay my hands on in a hurry. My father seems
to suspect us. He eludes to it in funny ways. You know what parents are
like. I think he saw you when you walked me home. Anyway, I don't
care what he thinks because I love you so completely. I will write to you,
care of John, and let you have the Singapore address, the moment we arrive.
Please take care my dear love, and write, when you can.*

I love you, your own dear Alexander.

I read and re-read the letter a dozen times, periodically looking at the
photograph. My friends stood on the far side of the room and watched,
and waited. All three began to cough and shuffle their feet which
brought me back to reality, or was it fantasy?

'It's from him, you know the boy I told you about, Alexander? It's
from him, the letter, it's from him.'

'I gather you've had a letter from him?' teased Joker.

'Yes, it's from him. It's his writing.'

'Oh put it away. Jesus, doesn't it want to make you throw up? Love?
Yuek! Makes me sick,' roared Biker, with faked disgust. *'It's from him.'*
He mimicked. 'The letter, it's from him, Oh my God it's from him.'

I picked up the nearest thing to come to hand which was a cushion,
and threw it at Biker. He caught it and threw it right back. So back I
threw it at Joker, who also started doing the mimicking. It was good
to see Angel laughing again. It was good to feel us all laughing. Despite
the teasing all three insisted on seeing the photograph and it was Angel
who summed up their silent approval;

'Very tasty! Nice one Poet!'

It was good that laughter was the first thing to happen in our bolt

98

hole. It broke the spell of the earlier tears in a way which all could understand and share in. I figured it had to be a good omen, so I sent out a prayer of thanks to a God I didn't believe in. The laughter allowed us to kind of unwind, alter the mood.

It wasn't long before we were sat drinking tea and planning who should sleep where. Biker and Joker decided that Angel and I should have the bed and that they would doss down in the lounge. Angel and I protested but gave in quickly when Biker said very softly that we had been through hell. We accepted. What a friend, he'd even sent his girl to his sisters' so that we could stay together.

Each of us piled what we had in the way of money on the coffee table. The pile from Biker, reminding us of where it came from, sent shivers through us all. But Biker made some joke about my letter and restored the good atmosphere. We had enough to get by for a couple of weeks, if we didn't go overboard on spending. We even had enough to rent a television set, Angel observed. So we agreed that we would.

Joker said that he really should contact his social worker to let him know that Angel was back. He told us this in a way which sought all our approval. So we all accepted it. The telephone in the flat was disconnected, so Joker went out to find one. He also took enough money for shopping. When he returned, I helped him unpack in the kitchen, whilst Angel and Biker read the comics he brought in with him. I could tell that Joker wanted to say something so I slowed down and waited.

'He wants to meet!'

'The social worker?'

'Yea, he says he'll meet anywhere, on my terms. He says he's concerned and that.'

'What did you say?'

'I'd think about it.'

'What's he concerned about? Angel?' I asked, attempting to make it easier for my friend to talk.

'I told him, you know, what happened to Angel and you, and he goes "I can find a decent children's home where you and Philip - that's Angel's real name - can stay together." So I said, yea I'll think about it. So he goes, "Let's meet and talk about things." I said I'll think about it.'

Joker's eyes searched mine unsure of my thoughts. So I reached out to touch him,

'Talking never did anyone any harm. Why don't you meet him?' I said, feeling that that's what my friend wanted anyway. 'I don't think

I'll be going back to London. I mean, I've had that place, you know?'

'I know what you mean. What are you going to do? Go home?'

'The Merch! The Merchant Navy! I may have to go home for a short time, but I think I'll join the Merch. How else am I going to get to see Alexander again?'

'He means that much to you?'

'He's kind of special, Joker. I've been thinking about it for some time. The strange thing is that the guy whose flat this is, Joseph, he suggested it to me when I first headed for London. It seems like a lifetime ago. Tennis John also said that it was a good idea. I guess had it not been for you and Angel I'd have left ages ago.'

'It was a lifetime ago. So much has happened. Do you remember when I first saw you on the Dilly?...'

'...And I asked you your name...?' I said, laughing.

'...And I said, "No names, no pack drill." I knew you were new. My name's Morris. Terrible isn't it? Makes me feel like a bleedin' car or something.'

'It's a great name, but you'll always be Joker to me. Joker the wise one! You took care of me Joker and I'll never forget you for that. Will you meet him?'

'We can't go on like this forever, can we? I mean, I want an education, don't I? But I want to stay with Angel.'

'You deserve it Joker! Besides Angel would always stick with you. He needs you as much as you need him.'

'If we could get into the same place, like he says, we could still be together and we'd be out of care in no time. I could go to college maybe? We could get a place.'

'You'd be good at that, and Angel will do as you do. He wants the best for you, you know that.'

Two days later, much still unspoken, yet somehow known about, it was Biker who broke the ice.

'I'm pissing off to my sisters'. No point in going back to London, right? I need my woman, right?'

'Right!' We all agreed.

'I'm thinking about joining the Merchant navy.' I ventured, looking at Angel.

Angel looked from me to Joker and asked, 'What about us?'

Joker hesitated, so I said, 'Why don't you see if you can get into a different kids home, together!'

The silence was deafening until Angel, still looking to Joker said, 'What about it Joker?'

'It's up to you, what do you think?'

Angel glanced to me. I smiled encouragement. Angel dropped his head and his whole body said,

'I've had the rent scene Joker.'

'You sure?' Joker asked, looking to Biker and me.

'Well I'm going to my sisters' and I'm taking the bleedin' car with me,' said Biker, determinedly. 'And Poet's joining the Merch. So that just leaves you two. You can't stay on the run forever, can you? Well, you can, but, I mean, where will it all end? Think about it Joker.'

'Only if we can stay together!' agreed Angel.

'Then I'll ring and arrange a meeting. What do you think, Angel? That okay with you?'

'Yea, sound. Let's do it.'

Relief swept through the flat and through all our hearts as Joker and Angel hugged each other. Tears filled my eyes as I headed for the kitchen to make more tea. They will be safe! That's all that matters!

Joker arranged to meet the social worker at the railway station in two days time and, if it was safe, to bring him back to the flat. Biker decided to take his leave the following morning so we all went down to the street to wave him farewell. It was sad to see a friend leaving, especially when in your heart of hearts you know you'll never see him again.

A day later, Angel and I tidy ourselves and wait for Joker to return with the social worker. I have no idea what a social worker is and am curious to meet one. I imagine he'll be posh and not have the faintest idea about the rent scene. While we wait, Angel and I stay within touching distance of each other. My mind, however, goes back to my early fantasy, when I was younger. I often escaped by going inwards, into my own imagination. I would convince myself that one day my real parents would come and rescue me from the life I'd been forced to live. So real was this desire that I could even transcend the pain of my father's belt, and escape into an inner world of colour. Perhaps sensing that I was some place else Angel puts his arms around me and reunited, we kiss, affectionately. We're still holding each other when the door opens and in comes Joker with the social worker. He's not in the least bit posh. His jeans and training shoes take me by surprise as does his greeting:

'You must be Poet? Joker told me all about you. Any chance of a cup of tea? I'm parched. My name's Andy by the way.'

Taking his outstreched hand I say something about being pleased to meet him and does he take sugar. Angel follows me into the kitchen and stays at my elbow while I make a pot of tea. Returning to the lounge we sit near Joker, on the opposite side of the room to Andy. It seems strange calling an adult, who's not a punter, by his first name. The atmosphere is tight with expectations.

'I hear you've had a rough time,' says Andy, to Angel and I, cutting through the small talk.

Angel touches me so I say,

'You could say that.'

'It's good that you had each other, then?'

I hear myself say, 'Yea.' I feel angry with myself for being so slow in the face of authority. I touch Angel. Angel says,

'What's the chances then?'

'Of finding you and Joker a new home? Pretty good I'd say. If that's what you both want.'

'What does it matter what we want?' asks Angel.

'Well, quite a lot, in fact. You've already proved that you can do a runner. So there's little point in sending, in finding, you a new place, if you're not happy there, is there? You'll leg it faster than before. You see, it's in all our interests to do the best we can. With me?'

'And if we don't like it?' suggests Angel, testingly.

'Let's take one step at a time. As I understand things you legged it, you left the other place because, well, because the other children found out about your sexual involvement with each other and one of the care staff.'

'So? Where's the harm in that?' snaps Angel. 'Everyone was screwing everyone else anyway. And we're not children!'

'Nothing was ever proved, but that member of staff was asked to resign, which he did without any fuss.'

'That's not our problem,' says Joker. 'You should be more concerned about who you employ. Kids have got enough to cope with.'

'Absolutely! I think you're right,' concedes Andy. 'The point is that we have a contact in Kent. A fabulous place, set in acres and acres of superb grounds, and we think we can get you in there. We know the staff and you won't have the same kind of problems there.'

'How's that? I mean, we can't stop being ourselves, can we? We can't just switch off,' laughs Joker.

'I'm not sure I follow you,' Andy says, gulping his tea.

'We are sexual, you know? We can't just stop being sexual, can we? You don't seem to understand, we actually enjoy having sex with other males. It's not just that we are on the rent. I think we can stop that, but we can't stop being turned on by other boys and men, can we?'

'So you're saying that you're all homosexual? Is that what you're saying?'

'Damn right!' barks Angel.

'Hang on a minute!' says Joker, furious. 'What I said was that we enjoy having sex with other males. It's you that wants to slap a label on that, not us. Why do you want to label things? Do you think you'll have some kind of control over it? Or what? Why can't you just accept what we say?'

'What else do you call it, if not homosexuality?' asks Andy reasonably. 'That's what it is!'

'That's crap!' shouts Joker. 'Describing the activity does not always mean you can apply the same description to the person doing the activity. That's too damn easy a cop out.'

'You've lost me.'

'When I do something homosexual it means that I am doing something homosexual. It does not mean that I have to be homosexual to enjoy it or do it. It may be that I am homosexual but that's for me to discover, not for you to speculate on! Look, labels are permanent, aren't they? They exclude everything else and once you've got it, you're stuck with it!'

Andy gulps his tea and nods his head.

'Okay, fair enough, I take your point. You're saying, let me see if I've got this right, you're saying, it's the activity which should be labelled, not the person. Because if we label the person then they are likely to be always stuck with it. Is that what you're saying?'

'Hole in one!' proclaims Joker. 'I mean, it's like you, 'aint it. You're a social worker right? And different people react to you because of the label, right? I mean, how many people really get to see you, the person? Not many I bet. I bet what they see is the label, right?'

'I have to confess you're right,'

This seems to satisfy Joker's need to be taken seriously and uniquely. He settles himself back into his chair and lights a cigarette. Angel and I wait for Andy to continue, as does Joker.

'Do I understand you correctly? Are you both concerned about being stuck with the label, homosexual?'

'I couldn't give a toss, one way or the other,' replies Angel, somewhat resigned. 'All I care about is that Joker and me aren't separated. I tell you now, if anyone tries, I'll be on my toes straightaway.'

'You have my word, you won't be separated,' says Andy, very seriously.

'Well, that's it, then,' Angel says, looking at Joker.

Joker, retaining eye contact with Angel, addresses himself to Andy,

'I want to go to college, or something. I don't want to go to no psychiatrists about being on the rent or about being queer. Get into all that and I'll be stuck with it until I get out of care.'

All eyes turned to Andy. He was nodding his head again.

'You're saying that you want to go into further education and not be held back by the things of the past. Is that it?'

'That's it!' Joker agrees.

'I can't promise anything. You know that reports have to be made, for your files. It is likely that you will have to speak to a therapist of some kind. Probably a psychiatrist. But, and this is an important but, I promise you that I will do everything in my power to get you onto a college course of some kind. I will also suggest that that's where the care effort should be placed, and not on seeing a psychiatrist on a regular basis. But, as I say, in the first instance, it is par for the course to see a psychiatrist in matters like this. Can you both accept that?'

'I'll do whatever Joker does,' answers Angel, guardedly.

'Joker?' questions Andy.

'I'm not sure. What do you think Poet?'

'I don't know Joker. I mean, I can do my own thing, can't I? You know, I can just go home and join the merch. I don't know what it's like being in-care.'

'I still want your opinion, Poet.'

'I know that you'd be really good at college and that you two have got to stick together. I know that you are two of the strongest people I've ever met and that you'd cope seeing whoever it is they ask you to see, just so long as you give your consent, and that's for you to decide. I mean, just say the word and we'll head off some place.'

Joker presses his bottom lip into his top lip and nods thoughtfully as I speak. He remains like that for a good two to three minutes before speaking. When he speaks, he is, as always, very decisive.

'Right, we'll go back with you and give it a go. But, and this is also an important but, any funny business and we're off. Deal?'

'Deal!' says Andy, shaking first Joker's hand, then Angel's.

We all laugh, but through it we know. This is it. This is the moment. Now I have to let go of two very special friends. It is a sudden realisation. A jolt to my consciousness, despite the fact that I knew it was coming from the moment Joker and I spoke in the kitchen. It is here, now. Suddenly I feel empty, lost. For the time we'd known each other, I'd taken my bearings from them and now they were going, together. Leaving friends must be the most difficult thing in the world for any person to do. It rips the heart to pieces and leaves one fragmented, incomplete. And me, terrified of just that, being incomplete, know that I'll pour myself into writing poem after poem into my notebook, in the hope of retaining the essense of what was. Already, in my imagination I am thinking in terms of the past tense. But the relief which filled my friends, injects me with a kind of hope, for them, for me, for us.

They want to end the stress of living on their wits and I want them to be happy. Sometimes, it seems, when you love someone you have to let them go, if you want the best for them. I force myself to think, to think beyond my own needs. I remind myself of those parents I've seen hanging on to their kids, not prepared to let them go to their own unique futures. They keep them, as kids, just in order to keep them. They rarely succeed, of course. The kids break away, and sometimes just don't return, let alone look back. On the other hand – there is always another side – I reflect that my own parents not only let me go from the nest too early but that they also never attempted to hang on emotionally. It was this not hanging on which left me always feeling unwanted, uncared for. It was this which was mainly to blame for me falling into the arms of any man who made a fuss of me. So desperate am I to be loved, that I would welcome the advance of any man, just so long as he was gentle and loving.

On reflection, I guess the sane way to let someone go is to do so with a hint of a genuine tear, with a warm hug and in the knowledge that one can return at anytime, should the need arise. But none of us live in an ideal world. We just have to make the most of whatever comes our way. But the whole damn process of grieving about what should have been is a lifetime's activity. It's not something one can do in a once and for all kind of way, if you know what I mean? Sometimes, when the opportunity comes along, like now, like when you have to say goodbye to friends, well, you just can't help but come face to face with emotions like grief and letting go. When these emotions burst onto the surface they bring with them all the other bits of unresolved grief and pain. So you have to relive them, you have no real say in the matter, do you? Because my folks let go of me in the way they did, more a kind of pushing away than letting go, I find letting go of those I love and care for the most difficult of things to do. You see, I want them to know, that as I let go, they are still loved, still wanted. It's always struck me as being crazy that to drive a car you have to pass a test to get a licence, but to bring a child into the world all you need do is fuck! I guess someday, when the world becomes overcrowded one will have to pass a test to become a parent! Perhaps then, the world won't be so screwed up about sex. You may think it kind of crazy, but I hope that one day people will enjoy sex for what it is, without wanting, without needing to describe it and themselves in a form acceptable to the majority.

I think Joker is right, that to even want to slap a descriptive label on a person, based on what they have so far been doing sexually, is more a measure of the insecurity of those slapping on the labels, than an accurate description of the person. It may not even be an accurate description of the action for that matter. The way I figure things, normal is defined by the biggest number, that's all. Anyone not conforming is therefore abnormal to them and will be encouraged or forced to step back in line. If they don't then they will either be banged up in prison or have another, more terrifying, label slapped onto them. That is, mental illness. Give me the uniqueness and individuality of daring caring people like Joker, Angel and Biker anytime before people who conform to every damn regulation in society's soul destroying rulebook. Even here, here on the page, I find myself hanging on to my friends, scared to move on. Instead, I ramble on about this and that, all the time avoiding letting them go. The truth? I'm scared to tell you what happens next. Perhaps, because if I tell you, I'll finally have to come to terms with things. But tell you I will, have no fear. I will finally share the truth.

Parting Gifts

Now it was agreed that Joker and Angel would go with Andy the following day, Andy went off, to book himself into a local hotel for the night. Having first taken us all out for a meal, he confidently waved us goodbye at the corner, saying he'd see us just after ten in the morning.

On the way back to Joseph's flat, Joker stopped outside a wine lodge and asked if we had enough for a bottle of wine. We had more than enough. Biker had seen to that before leaving. He'd split up the money he'd taken from the vermin. I had enough to get me back to Liverpool, with some to spare. We bought two bottles of French red and uncorked both the moment we got back. We toasted each other and the future. Joker toasted the rent scene and all the boys who would 'come' after us. Angel and I fell about laughing and begged Joker to do a Winston

Churchill for us. Joker cleared his throat, raised his glass and went instantly into his Churchill voice:

'Andy, our esteemed social worker is a nice man, a good man no less. Above all else he is sincere, would you not agree? Yes, of course he is. Well, my friends, let me tell you what a member of parliament, a man by the name of Tom Driberg, once wrote on the subject, way back in the late 30's. Then ask yourselves what account we should take of this sincere social worker's sincerity. Is sincerity all that is needed to convince us? Tom Driberg commented that, "...Sincerity is all that counts. It's a widespread modern heresy. Think again. Bolsheviks are sincere. Fascists are sincere. Lunatics are sincere. People who believe the earth is flat are sincere. They can't all be right. Better make certain first you've got something to be sincere about and with..." So, what is it that our esteemed sincere social worker is being sincere about? Could it be, might it just perhaps be that he is being sincere about being sincere, so that we can then think of him as being sincere. I sincerely hope not but sincerely believe so. And a wiser man than Driberg, a man by the name of George Bernard Shaw, said that, "...It is dangerous to be sincere unless you are also stupid..." Is our esteemed sincere social worker stupid? I think not. I do, however, sincerely believe that he thinks we are. There can only be one measure of sincerity and that is that, like the earth, but unlike Bolsheviks, fascists, lunatics and social workers, it is round. That it comes back and joins into itself is the measure, not how one sounds. Now, to close and before you applaud, lest you think me insincere in using quotes let me tell you what the great man, Winston Churchill himself, said on the matter. He said, "...It is a good thing for an uneducated man to read books of quotations..." And surely there can be no doubt that I am the least educated here. But, my friends, I know enough, at least, to know how to learn.'

Joker stopped and with a huge sweeping gesture bowed. Angel and I applauded and I said that I thought the performance was absolutely brilliant, and that he was the wisest person I'd ever met. Angel just hung around Joker's neck and kissed him, affectionately.

When the last of the wine was in our glasses Angel asked Joker if he really thought that Andy was trying to pull the wool over our eyes.

'Perhaps not consciously. I mean, he might be okay himself. But it's obvious that once he gets us back there, well, it's out of his hands then and the big machine takes over, right?'

'So what do we do?' asked Angel, confused. 'Do we go back with him or what?'

Joker sipped his wine thoughtfully, then said,

'Yea. Yea, we'll go back. I mean, it might be okay. But if they split us up, even for one night, we get on our toes the first chance we get. If that happens, if we do a runner after we've been split up, head for the Dilly and we'll meet up there, okay? Remember Angel it's us who are going to decide what happens from now on, and no one else, right?'

'Right!' enthused Angel, relieved. 'And tonight belongs to us. Let's make it a night to remember. Let's go to bed, the three of us.'

Perhaps the best measure of any friendship are the inhibitions which exist between those involved. With Joker, Angel and myself, if there were any inhibitions, they very soon became a thing of the past. When we climbed naked into the bed we wanted only what was to come, each other. We'd often done this before but it had nearly always been for the benefit of a punter. This time it was to be a celebration of our friendship. It was for us. It was our most precious gift, each for the other. It was our parting gift. We knew of no more precious a gift to give, than ourselves. What more could we give? What else could we have given? If there was something else, how could we have known about it?

Our love making is unashamed, pulsing male loving, with each of us becoming the centre at various times. When one becomes the centre the other two work on him to bring him all the joy and pleasure we can. With ease, we change around. There is no passive or active partner. Instead, and far more naturally, we are three friends loving each other in the most sensuous way possible. Over the years, we've learnt our individual crafts well and here, for the first time, we share and learn more. We care and aren't poor. Every action producing another. Every gesture flowing fluently from the previous gesture, unthought, unaided by effort. All three moving, becoming one. Then two and then one, and then three. Effortlessly moving into the other, blending and altering taste and form. Here we are beyond all rules and regulations. Beyond even ourselves. We give ourselves up to the moment and go where it leads. Here we are unafraid for it takes us only to the greater glory of uncharted freedoms, safely, without judgement. Here boys can love boys fully and with their own consent. When sleep comes, it too flows out of what was.

In the morning, when I return from the bathroom, the vision of my two beautiful friends fills me with love. Colours dance through my mind and my heart, uncontrolled and spontaneous. I see only beauty. As they slowly wake, outstretched arms welcome me back into the space between them. I kiss each and tell them that whatever happens to us, I'll always love them. They embrace me and we fall into the contented silence which follows all creative love making. None of us wants to move and are only forced to do so by a knock on the door. We hold each other even tighter and let our silent eyes do the talking. They say, "You are my friend! You are part of me! You will always be my friend!"

Only then do we jump from the bed and grab our clothes, the outer garments of conformity. I have to force myself to dress, to pull on the conformity which disguises my true identity. When Andy enters, we are once again, the respectable teenage boys he left the evening before. Sadness creeps through the flat like a preying monster, infecting us all. It bites huge chunks out of our confidence and I have to think consciously about the love we generated the night before, for it's slipping away, even now, into memory. Now, afraid to catch each other's eyes, for fear we'll once again want to regain the love, we busy ourselves, packing. Andy too, sensing the monster, makes tea in the kitchen. When he serves it, he slips me a piece of paper on which he's written my friends' new address and his own telephone number. I nod my head in gratitude and sip the tea. Andy passes around cigarettes and opens his newspaper. He at least has found a way to escape. I let my eyes wander around the flat which has brought me so much joy. Here I encountered Alexander, Joseph and my two special friends. I look around and wander if part of the love we created here will somehow stay and become part of the fabric. I look at Joker. What a daft nickname for one so wise. I look at Angel. What a delicately strong boy he is. I look at Andy and my eyes fall on his newspaper. There down in the corner of the front page is a photograph, a face I know. I jump to my feet and grab the paper from Andy's hand and stare at the face. The others, confused, look to each other for an explanation, while I look at the face of Brixton Billy, the young black kid who'd asked me for a cigarette on The Meat Rack.

Before I read the article, I somehow knew what it would say. I force myself to read it. It tells me that the semi-clothed body of a boy was found in a shallow grave in Kent and that the police have begun a murder hunt. When my hands fall to my sides and the paper from my hands, air gushes from my lungs and I fall backwards into the chair. When eventually I'm able to respond to the concerned questions of my friends, I tell them that I'd once met Billy and that he could have been anyone of us.

I shudder and shake inside. I scream at the top of my voice but nothing comes out. Neither Joker nor Angel knew Billy but nonetheless they too are devastated by the news that he was one of us, a rent boy. Not the first to be killed, but the first one we had met. That kind of brings things home to you, you know? We can distance ourselves from stories in the press but we can't quite do the same when we've met the person. I hear his voice in my head saying how cool it was. I see him stride away from me into the crowds and I see him going to his death. I am gripped with rage and remorse. Why hadn't I taken him under my wing the way Joker had with me? If I had then perhaps he wouldn't now be dead. Rent boys should stick together, help each other out. In my arrogant selfishnes I'd not taken the kid into the protective circle which I myself had found. I tell this to those in the room and it's Andy who answers. He says something about not blaming myself, that it was out of my control. That if it hadn't have been this kid then it would have been another. I know he's right but I also know that he's wrong.

'Rent boys,' he continues, 'must be one of the most neglected 'at risk' groups in the country today and yet nothing is done to help them or understand them. Not one penny of Government money is spent. We close our eyes to these things because we can't face the truth. We, social workers, politicians, everyone in society, all of us adults with the vote, we are more at fault than you Poet.'

'He's right Poet!' says Joker. 'Who gives a toss!' Come on Poet, you know he's right. It's crazy to blame yourself because others turn a blind eye.'

'I know he's right but I could have taken the kid under my wing, just like you did for me Joker, it's as simple as that!'

'You're assuming the kid wanted that, aren't you?' asks Joker pointedly.

'Perhaps!' I concede.

'Perhaps nothing! Be honest, look back and ask yourself if that's what the kid seemed to want or need? Come on Poet, be honest.'

'Maybe not. He was a cocky little sod, a nice kid. No, he didn't want looking after, he struck me as kind of vulnerable though.'

'Which rent boy isn't?' says Angel, taking my arm. 'All of us are, aren't we?'

'I guess, it's just such a terrible waste. He was just a kid, you know?'

'We know Poet, honestly, we know,' says Joker, standing up and taking hold of his bags.

In a strange kind of way, it is somehow fitting that our parting is shrouded in grief. It is anyway, but now we have a more legitimate reason for our tears. At Andy's car, we kiss and hug and I cry, promising to write and let them have my address. They climb into the car and within minutes it is pulling away. The faces of my friends in the rear window, smiling, crying, laughing, encouraging, blowing kisses, being strong, get smaller and smaller until they are eventually out of sight.

Back in the flat, I take all my clothes off and climb back into the bed which still has the fresh boy smell of my friends, to keep me company.

Prison Strokes

When I wake from my misty sleep I do so with a kind of regret for, in leaving my sleep, I leave my dreams. Dreams of boyhood friends and loyalty. Dreams of overcoming hurdles with the kind of ease facilitated only by dreams. I discovered long ago that dreams are little more than contrasting compensating signposts pointing the way to survival. Either that or total nightmares. Dreams make powerful the powerless and sometimes in a terrifying way. Fortunately, as a child, my dreams took me into a world of Cowboys and Indians, goodies and baddies. By whatever saving mechanism, I was nearly always a Cowboy. Cowboys, you see, were always the goodies then. At least, that's what the messages in the picture house told me. Nightmares, though, are like health warnings, those things I should fear most; mostly my father or being trapped in endless rooms with countless doors, leading to further rooms and further doors. Sometimes, nightmares warn me about my potential negative self. The self which uses violence and hate. These kind of nightmares are the worst of all because they feed off that bit of me which works hard to deny that I can be violent.

Strangely, since I actually came close to killing that rapist, I've kind of accepted, thanks to Biker, that I can be as violent as anyone else and the nightmares have all but stopped. It's as though in recognising my own violent potential I've gained more control over it and myself. I know that I have the ability or power to kill, so I don't need to have empowering dreams about it anymore, at least that's the hope. There's always hope, right?

Hugging a pillow to my bare chest I try hard to smell the love which has been shared in this bed. Perhaps, though, I'm only trying to hang on to people who've gone. It's really strange the way people come and go in life. It's as though I'm on a one way street and everything is going the same way, some faster than others. That's how we meet, one overtaking the other. Get in the way and get trampled. You never meet people coming the other way, coming back. Everyone is going someplace, any place is a better place to be, right? Why the hell don't we all just stop for a day and talk to each other? Perhaps because the truth would scare everyone too much, that most everyone is on a journey away from themselves.

Adults dash around trying to convince each other that where they're going is 'the place to be' and some adults and kids follow blindly, generation after generation of them, believing that the place to be is where the seemingly strong adults are. The more that follow, the more the self-elected leaders believe themselves to be right. They don't just believe it, they know it! For the way is signposted for them by previous travellers. Most of the signs read, 'Money and Power'. While others, just to spice things up a bit, read 'Power and Money'. The only requirement along the way is for each traveller to keep the signs painted and pointing in the right direction, away from self. That way the signs become places of homage and everyone feels safe in the knowledge that it's perfectly okay to live in order to take. Somehow, there's something more honest and proper in being a rent boy who takes in order to live.

Throwing the now contaminated pillow to the far side of the bed I fling back the bedclothes and survey my nakedness. What others find attractive eludes me. My hair is straight and blond, my eyes blue and my skin fair. The tuft of pubic hair below my belly is how I'd like the hair on my head, darker and curly. Why is pubic hair always curly? I run my fingers through it and I'm amazed at just how springy it is. My other hand explores the hair on my head. The contrast is strange. The small amount of hair under each arm is different again. I search for the signs of body hair on my chest and find none. I feel my face and know that it will be many years before I have to start shaving. My lower legs have some hair but being blond they are barely visible. It's really strange as the eyes in my old head look down on the flesh of the young boy. I know it's strange, for the boy should see the boy, right? What I see is myself as the object all punters see. An object for their pleasure. Am I as beautiful as they tell me? Is my smooth naked flesh as fine as the ivory they speak of? Is my growing erection a sign of my own needs or is it a response to theirs? The pulsing between my legs demands that I move so that it stands flat against my belly. It demands to be touched. Instantly, my mind's eye is full of the glorious colour of Alexander. His hands slide into mine and become ours.

I hear his voice in my head and let his hands slide over my bed warm flesh. I feel his full voluptuous lips on mine while his fingers wrap themselves around the proof that I am one hundred per cent male. As they close around me so my hips move in perfect harmony towards each downward stroke. Rolling on my side I feel myself entering him, the firmness of his cheeks forming the shapes to which I unquestioningly unite. My hips press forward, our hands stroke ever faster, my breathing finds a new purpose as I call out, pulse out his name, over and over and over again. Later, in the bathroom, I catch sight of myself in the mirror to find my face blushed with unashamed joy.

The time is upon me now. I must act on my plan to join Alexander. The plan, as you know, is simple enough, I'll join the Merchant Navy, take a ship bound for Singapore and... That's as far as I dare imagine for the time being. So, what now? I have to return to London for a couple of weeks at least to get some funds together. I can't bring myself back to Liverpool flat broke. Call it pride for that's what it is but I don't want folks to see me as a loser. When my feet hit Liverpool's streets they must be in new shoes.

Before leaving Farnborough I rang Tennis John to ask him if I could stay for a couple of weeks. He didn't hesitate for a second. Nor, as you can guess, did he ask any questions;

'My dear boy the room will be ready for you.'

So it was too! Clean sheets, fresh flowers and a card on the pillow to welcome me back. I returned his gift by walking about the flat with as few clothes on as possible. Sometimes, quite naked. When I told him more fully of my plans to join the Merchant Navy, John suggested that there was no need for me to return to Liverpool;

'Why go to Liverpool? My dear boy, you can join from here. You can use this address.'

'But won't it cause problems for you? I don't even know how to go about it.'

'Problems? Not in the least! I am, how do you say, insulated from such things. I will get you all the details on how you go about joining tomorrow, now relax.'

I was delighted and dashed off to my room to get into my tennis whites. Returning to the lounge I was thrilled to see the pleasure in John's eyes.

'My dear boy... Thank you... You look beautiful.'

Over the next three weeks, with John's help, I'd completed the application forms, had an interview and been accepted into training at some place in Gloucester called Sharpness. In just two months time I was to join the training ship 'Vindicatrix' and a whole new way of life.

113

Eager to share the news with Joker and Angel I telephoned the social worker, Andy.

'Poet? I'm glad you phoned.'

'Yes I've got good news for Joker and Angel...'

'Poet listen, you could have serious problems...'

'What? Are they okay? Where are they?'

'I'm not allowed to say but listen...'

'What are you talking about? Not allowed, you promised...'

'It's out of my hands...'

'You promised...'

'Poet you could have syphilis!'

'What!'

'I'm sorry to be so frank about this Poet but you have to get yourself to a V.D. clinic as soon as possible. The simple facts are that both Joker and Angel are infected and...'

'Where are they? I have to speak to them myself...'

'It's just not possible, I'm sorry. Will you go for a check-up?'

'Of course I'll go! Will you give them a message?'

'I'm sorry Poet, I have strict instructions...'

'You're full of shit! You promised...'

'I'm sorry Poet...'

In my rage I all but buried the telephone handset into its cradle. Joker was right! The social worker's sincerity was a blind. Joker and Angel would soon realise and get the hell out of wherever it was they were being held. There could be no doubt about it, they were being held against their will. There could be no doubt also that at the first opportunity they'd be on their toes.

The following day I made my way to the clap clinic, terrified. Not of having clap but of the very experience. The unknown is always the biggest fear. I told the doctor that I thought I might have syphilis and that I was a rent boy. I was asked to undress and he examined my hands and feet and then said;

'You're right but we'll do further tests to confirm things.'

The last parts of my body I imagined would be examined were my hands and feet. When I asked why I was told that there could be spots just under the skin, like a rash below the surface. The other tests were more in keeping with my expectations. They took swabs from my cock, throat and backside. I gave a urine sample and thirty minutes later the first diagnosis was confirmed. The treatment amounted to coming in every day for two weeks to be given an injection, and to avoid all sexual contact. They also asked me to see a social worker but I refused point-blank. They insisted. I stood firm. They explained that they needed to contact those people I'd had sex with. I told them I didn't have their names. They let it go at that. One name, however, echoed deep within me, Alexander.

So, each morning, for the following two weeks, I'd go in, have the injection and spend the rest of the day hanging around the Dilly. I tried hard not to think of Alexander but each day I saw him in my soul, unaware that he might have a sexually transmitted disease. Could life be that cruel? I knew it could! Two weeks later, all the injections and tests complete, I was given a clean bill of health. I felt terrible! Nothing more horrible could have happened, than through an act of love, I could have infected the very person I loved so much. And, as yet, I'd not heard from him and knew of no way to make contact. I felt very sick and told myself that I had to take charge of my life and get off the rent scene.

However, that night, I discovered that there is a huge universe between the world of intention and the world of resolution. You can take the rent boy out of the scene but you can't take the scene out of the rent boy. The truth of the matter is that I did a fifty pound punter who paid upfront before the action. He screwed me till it hurt. So bad did I feel about myself that I kind of enjoyed the pain and the punter became even more turned on by my tears. So much so that he gave me an extra twenty quid and begged to see me again. I told him that I never went with the same man twice and besides I prefered boys my own age. He became hooked on this and offered ridiculous amounts of money to join in the action with me and another boy. In an attempt to get rid of him I asked for five hundred pounds. He never flinched when he agreed. The guy had the hots and he also had the money to back it up. I agreed to see him the following night. Let's face it, five hundred pounds is a King's ransom to a fifteen year old rent boy. All I had to do was to find another rent boy. Shouldn't be much of a problem, right? I mean, what rent boy would turn down two hundred and fifty quid? None!

I found a boy my own age the following day who agreed to take part for half the loot. The kid thought he'd come up on the pools and was getting high on what had come his way. I told him that his excitement would put the punter off and that he had to act like he wasn't enjoying it and that when he got screwed to cry if he could. The kid had been around and played his part to perfection. The punter was well pleased.

Afterwards, when we'd all bathed and had a few drinks the punter offered us both an envelope. I was content to wait until we left to count my loot but the other kid opened his straight off.

'What the fuck's this?' He said, first to the punter and then to me. 'This some kind of fucking rip off or what?'

I tore open my envelope and counted the money. Fifty pounds!

'This is not what we agreed. The deal was five hundred pounds.'

The punter filled our glasses and smiled as he put the bottle on the table between us. He appeared quite confident when he said,

'Don't let's play games. You both have fifty pounds each, more than either of you ever normally get, so let's just call it quits shall we?'

He was right of course, a fifty pound punter was a dream come true. But...

'The fuck with you, shithead! You told this kid five hundred and that's what you're going to pay, got it?' Exploded my new found partner.

'Wrong! Do yourself a favour now and put it down to experience.' As he spoke, so he stood and indicated that we should leave.

I stood, defeated and ready to go. What else was there to do? The answer to that came as the bottle crashed and shattered into the side of the punter's head. Blood danced a crazed pattern through the air, as though in slow motion, and the punter followed it, in the same manner. He crashed against the wall with such a force that pictures jumped from it and fell around the bloodied shell on the floor. The situation, already insane, was made worse by the screams that followed. First, the violent angry screams of the kid as he hit the punter. Then the punter's sickening cry as the bottle hit his head. Followed by my own horror as I saw the blood spurt from the huge gash in the man's head. Instantly, as though seeking answers, there was a deafening silence. The kid looked to me, I looked to the punter and the punter looked to the kid. I had to take the initiative;

'Jesus Christ! What the fuck did you do that for?'

Before I'd finished asking the question I realised that the kid had no answer. It had been a reflex action to being cheated. It was, in many ways, no different to my own reaction when I'd wanted to kill that scum in the warehouse. It was this thought which governed my next actions, regretfully.

'Let's get the hell out of here!'

The kid, however, had other ideas. He dropped the broken bottle and went searching through the punter's home. For what? Money, I guess. As he did so the punter looked to me, and I felt his pain.

'I'll call an ambulance!' was all I could say. The punter indicated his gratitude, which made me feel even worse. I wanted to tell him that

116

I didn't really know the kid, that he wasn't a friend or anything like that, that I wanted no part of what he'd done. But I knew it was far too late for that. I grabbed my coat and made for the door, the kid joined me with his loot. Despite what the kid had done, I felt I was with the right person. We belonged together. He was an idiot, sure. But he was a rent boy. Never had I been so torn inside. I wanted to stay and help the punter. God knows, that's what I should have done. Instead, I identified with another rent boy, and took to my heels.

Damn it, I know I was wrong, but who the hell is a rent boy in trouble supposed to rely upon, if not another rent boy? How is it possible to be both right and wrong at the same time? It was right to go and it was right to stay. Fate, perhaps aware of my conflict, took charge and found a way to resolve the problem. As we opened the front door we ran straight into the arms of two coppers walking past. I have to confess to feeling great relief as it became obvious to the coppers that the kid's pockets were full of stolen loot. Within the hour we were both banged up in the police station.

We were both charged with G.B.H. and theft and because I once again followed the lead of the kid, and stupidly pleaded not guilty, we were both remanded in custody to the young person's unit at Brixton prison, while the police completed their enquiries.

To get us to the prison we were both handcuffed and placed in a prison van. The van, more the size of a bus, had a narrow passageway running its full length. On either side were small individual cells about eighteen inches square. There was just enough room to sit on the bare wooden bench. The tiny window was darkened so that people couldn't see in. When the door was closed shut, I was gripped with a great fear of such a tiny space. If the vehicle crashed there could be little hope for those of us locked in. Old dreams of being shut up, trapped and unable to get out, flooded my mind with vivid childhood pictures. To cope with this, I reminded myself that I had only myself to blame for getting into such a mess in the first place. I'd done wrong and now I must pay for it. I had no right whatsoever to complain about the consequences. When we got back to court I would plead guilty.

Prison is a depressing place. Its dark Victorian structure seems to infect all who enter, including the staff. Being in the control of such people is even more depressing for mostly they lack any sense of what it is to be human and give the most basic of instructions as though to vacant animals: 'Strip, bathe, put these on, no talking, stand over there.' They strut and pose like prize peacocks and rattle their keys in the hope that all the world can hear their authority. What sad and pathetic creatures they are as they work so hard to impress only each other!

I look to my fellow prisoners and suspect, from the eye contact, that we are all prisoners here. The only difference between the guards and ourselves being that the guards came here because they wanted to, they wear different clothes and they carry keys. We, on the other hand, are here because we have been sent. Watching the behaviour of the guards leads me to believe that the essential ingredient required to be a prison guard is the need to have power over others. And, it is only powerless people who therefore fit the bill. In this sense, they are not very different to those they guard.

I'm banged in a cell by myself, by a guard who doesn't look into my eyes, and told that the bed is only to be used at night. During the day it should be folded up against the wall. The cell is about ten feet square, has tiled walls, a cold hard floor and a window too high to see out of. Apart from the bed, already folded in the required position, the only other items are a small crude wooden table and chair and a chamber pot. I could be in the last century. The only sounds are boots on concrete, jangling keys and doors slamming. I try the chair and find it very uncomfortable. The bed seems more attractive so I try that. Perfectly scripted, for they know how the story goes, a guard appears at the peephole in the door and screams at me to get off the bed. I hear the delight in his voice and the hate in my heart.

With no books, no writing material, no smokes, I'm banged up for twenty three hours a day. Food is brought to the cell and not only do the guards continue not to look me in the eye, they also don't speak. They stand and watch as the prisoner hands a tray to me. I realise that if they look at me in the eye, they'll see me. That's obviously the last thing they want to do so they look at the actions of the tray passing from one hand to another. There is little to do apart from eat, sleep and play with myself. Masturbation must be the most common therapy, the best form of relief from prison. The art, I soon discover, is to wank slowly and not come for a long time. The longer the wank the more relief and comfort one gets. Prison wanking becomes not a sexual act but a mental and emotional one. It's a sanity saving device. It's about giving oneself comfort in a heartless dehumanised environment. I wank all the time. At least up until the time when, out of the blue, I'm given some smokes, a book and some writing material. The smoke is hand rolling tobacco. I learn quickly to roll the smokes very thinly and to split the matches into four. The book is a crappy western, but I read every damn word at least three times. With the writing material I write to Tennis John. Within days he visits me and brings some decent books, smokes and

118

writing paper. He tells me that a letter has arrived from Singapore. I ask him to keep it for me.

I try to explain to John what it's like to be banged up for twenty three hours each day, day in, day out. Week in, week out.

'Try sitting in a bare room for a couple of days, you'll discover what I mean.'

Fortunately, within weeks I appeared at court with the other kid and we both pleaded guilty. The waiting was over. Tennis John came as a character witness and told the judge that I was due to go into training in the Navy. The judge said he'd take that into account and fined me fifteen pounds. The other kid was fined forty pounds. John paid my fine and took me for a slap-up meal. He was, as always, unquestioning, unjudging and totally reliable.

In the comfort of my bed that night I find that I'm unable to sleep or open the letter from Singapore. I place the letter on the bedside table and stare at it, full of self-loathing. Thoughts invade my head from my heart as I shift from side to side in a bid to shake them. Still my eyes stay on the letter. I can't bring myself to open it! My emotions are just too sharp as my life in London replays itself in my head. In the time I've been in London, and still not sixteen years old, I've been tortured and raped, come close to killing a man, had syphilis, most likely infected Alexander, a young black rent boy has been murdered, I've had the brothers grim on my trail and I've tasted prison life. Yet, in my heart of hearts, I feel that I'm not a bad person. Or, am I just fooling myself? You tell me, I'm too confused to work it out. I mean, if I am just bad, then how did I get that way in the first place? And if I am bad then perhaps I should just work at being bad. You know, get really *good* at it.

At three o'clock in the morning I sit bolt upright in bed, sweating and panting. I realise, then, that instead of getting off with a small fine I could now be serving life for murder. The man could have been killed by that bottle crashing into his skull and just by being there, I would have been judged just as guilty as the other kid. Jesus, I have to get out of this way of living! The Merchant Navy could not have come at a better time. I've really had the rent scene and all the crap which goes with it.

Don't get me wrong here. I'm not so much hung up about having sex for money as I am about putting up with the crap which goes with it. It's the way of living which is the problem not the selling of sex. Damn it, everybody sells something of themselves, whatever they do. Everyone's on the game! I put my head back into the pillow in the hope that the rent scene and I are heading for a divorce, a trial separation at least.

With new found courage I open the letter from Singapore the following morning:

My Dearest Richie,

How I miss you. Have you any idea? I do so love you and think of you all the time. Do you think of me? If you love me even half as much then that is enough. The situation here is impossible. My father constantly refers to you in ways which lead me to believe that he knows more than he should. I've told him nothing, of course. I've had some kind of infection in the nether regions but after lots of injections it's all cleared up now. That's Singapore for you. They kept me in bed for a couple of weeks, which was very boring. Especially when I really didn't feel ill. But rest assured, I'm as fit as a fiddle and very healthy. To be on the safe side of things it might be better to keep what you have to say in your letters very simple. My father is a pain. I'll work out a code and send you a copy when it's done. Then we can say whatever we want without having to concern ourselves about others. I love you, write soon.

Your own Alexander.

I was still crying my tears of joy when John came into my room with a breakfast tray. I handed him the letter. He read it then hugged me and said,

'My dear boy, all will be well. Such a love will find its own solution.'

As he spoke I prayed that he was right. However, experience warned me it was impossible. Nonetheless, I wrote back that same day, with hope in my heart.

The Vindi

Never before in my life have I encountered the symbolic meaning of packing my bags. With each garment, neatly folded, and placed in the case, I sense a piece of me leaving London and heading for Singapore. I sense, too, I am saying goodbye to the rent scene forever. So intense are the feelings of letting go that I find my physical movements being slowed by a call from deep within my soul. Savour this moment. Never forget this moment. Experience it as deeply as you can, for as long as possible. Such moments, I know, are rare and delicate.

The last item to be packed is the notebook I've had little time to write in of late. I hold it as one would, as one should, hold something fragile and precious, and allow myself to flick through its now well thumbed pages. In a strange way, I feel that I'm holding myself, reading myself. A sudden truth dawns upon me, when those days emerge when I'm too busy to write something in my little book then I'm doing the wrong thing with those days. That's the way things have been of late, right? No time to think or to write. I feel obliged, for my own well being and peace of mind, to write something in the notebook. This:

Good-Buy Rent Boys

Goodbye goodbuy goodlay boys,
Only time to stop the ploys, then
Onwards, towards a new ontology.

Delustred lights greet Soho youth, while
Blustered nights speak Soho truth of
Utopian dreams amid usury screams.

You'll always be my Hellenic brother, so
Remember me who broke from cover, away from
Entombed hopes made fast by ropes.

Neptune sings a song to please,
Tidings of great victories, of a
Boy for sale who sails for a boy.

Our paths will cross in time ahead, but know,
Your truth, know it speaks, it will be said.
So long my friends. So long my friends.

Placing the sanity saving notebook in the case, I hesitate before closing the lid, feeling that I'm turning my back on those more like me than any other group I'll encounter at the training school. It's a kind of guilt. Nonetheless, I shut the lid and fasten it with absolute conviction and feel relieved.

Not wanting a long goodbye at the station, I bid my farewells to John at his front door and climb into a cab. When we've turned the corner I ask the cab driver to drive through Soho and around Piccadilly Circus. Faces and scenes I know well flash past as I say my silent goodbyes to them. This place will remain etched on my soul, in my heart of hearts I know this. I know too that I'll take it with me wherever I go, just as I still carry much of my childhood and too much of Ireland and Liverpool.

I like the train, for it moves further and faster away from London by the minute. I know that people say that life is a journey but I only ever become aware of that when I'm travelling myself. It doesn't matter much what the vehicle is. It's the physical sensation of moving mixed up with longed-for hopes of what might be, that's what matters most. It's a kind of freedom. Perhaps, too, it's a kind of wishful thinking. *I wish, I wish, I wish in vain, I wish I were quite pure again. But, pure again, I ne'er can be, till apples grow on an orange tree. Perhaps, though, around the next bend, over the next hill, in the next field, perhaps there, clouded in mystery, is an orange tree with apples on it.*

At Gloucester I have to change trains for Sharpness and when I do, I can begin to pick out the other boys also heading for the training school. We crowd politely onto the small train, avoiding each other's glances. I count about fifty boys and hear plenty of Liverpool accents. It's anyone's guess as to how long we'll remain polite with each other, for the other dominant accent comes from the mouths of boys from Glasgow. As the train moves out so the banter begins. Boys fall neatly into familiar groups. Scouses with scouses, Jocks with Jocks. I keep my mouth firmly shut and look out of the window. In the reflection of the window, I see a boy doing the same thing and venture a smile.

His returning smile, a long time coming, is accompanied by a movement of the head, towards the noise in the corridor, which seems to say that he wants no part of the factions around him. I nod in agreement. He smiles again and we both return to our window views.

At Sharpness we are met by an officer from the training school who looks very impressive in his uniform. Our names are called and we take our place on a waiting coach. I find an empty seat, avoiding both the Scouses and the Jocks, sensing that one should take time and check out the members before joining any group. Identifying with people instantly, just because they come from the same city, strikes me as a serious sign of insecurity. But, there again, I guess it's understandable. Besides, I remind myself, I'm a seasoned veteran traveller. My reward for this act of independence is that the smiling boy from the train joins me, offering his hand as he does.

'Hi, I'm Sean. I heard your name being called, you're Richard?'

'Richie.' I correct as my new found companion takes his seat beside me.

'Richie, right. Pleased to meet you Richie.' He says, offering his hand.

As our hands join so our eyes meet and are held for that length of time undetectable to observers but long enough for us to know we have met someone special. It emerges that Sean is a first born American boy of Irish parents, so we hit it off instantly. His accent is a blended mixture of Irish and soft American. We chat about the problems of being born in a strange country. We have much in common.

At the training school we are split into groups. Just as on the train, the Scouses are to be with fellow Scouses and the Jocks are to be with Jocks. To my relief, because I joined from London, I'm put with the remaining group, and therefore with Sean. We stand close together, letting others know that we intend to stay that way.

The training school is more like an army camp than a school. The accommodation is in huts, of which there are some twenty or so. There is a parade ground and the essential flagpoles. Boys, wearing army uniform, dyed dark blue, are being marched from one place to another, by instructors in smart naval uniforms. The camp holds close to five hundred boys all more or less the same age. At the far side of the camp, and down a steep incline, berthed in an enclosed dock on the very edge of the river Severn, is the training ship, The Vindicatrix. Efficiency and order dominate. White painted kerbs around each hut gleam, as does everything else. Each hut houses about forty boys in bunk beds. Sean and I secure a bunk at the end of the hut. Between the huts are smaller huts, the latrines. Each latrine being shared by two huts. The other huts are for training. One hut is a church, one a picture house. Within a couple of hours of arriving we are in uniform, have cleaned the hut, been inspected by our instructor and have had a welcoming talk from the Captain. He explains that for the two months or so that we are here we will be trained fully, some as deck hands, some as stewards. Sean and I are to be stewards. During his talk he mentions that Tommy Steele was trained here some years ealier. As things turn out, Sean has his old bunk.

At the end of the first day, because we are the new intake, we are subjected to a considerable amount of good natured teasing from the other boys, especially from those just one intake ahead of us. We learn much in the teasing about what it means to live in such large numbers. We are told of the 'anti-wank' which is said to be put in the chocolate drink at night. We learn, too, that not to be part of one of the two dominant groups is to be subject to the abuse of both. Fights are organised between the Jocks and Scouses on an almost day to day basis, behind a hut, after lights out. Those caught fighting, however, are made to box each other in front of the whole camp. There is much talk of sex and much boasting about who's done what. I figure the place must be a hotbed of sexual activity. Five hundred boys locked together for months can't all rely on their own right hand, surely? Before being bedded down for the night an instructor informs us that we must wash before bed and that pyjamas must be worn without underclothes.

After washing, the instructor made us all stand by our bunks and told us that he was going to inspect us. He walked down the line of boys and pulled open the front of each boy's pyjama trousers. Those still wearing their shorts were told to take them off, instantly. Experience on the rent scene told me instantly that here was a punter if ever I'd seen one. The pleasure he gained watching half naked boys obeying his orders, though disguised by a poker face, was all too apparent to me. So, when he got to me I unfastened the cord around my waist and let the trousers fall wide open. He froze. I kept them open and looked straight into his eyes. I must beat this guy at his own game. When his eyes eventually shifted to meet my own, I winked. He looked back to my cock, which I gave a twitch to. His face became almost scarlet. When he looked up I winked again. He quickly went on to the next boy, and the next. When he finally left the hut he was the colour of beetroot. He knew he'd been sussed and never again did he inspect us that way.

The discipline in the camp was nothing like that of the army. Boys and instructors generally got on very well together. The most serious punishment was to be put on jankers. This meant going down to the training ship and doing some spud bashing for a couple of hours in the evening, while everyone else enjoyed themselves. Everyone did it from time to time. It was no big deal. In fact, in the company of a friend it was a pleasure. With a friend you got through the spud bashing fairly quickly and could then sit around and have as much tea and toast as you wanted. It was an evening such as this, alone with Sean that we got to know each other better. He suggested that we go for a walk, away from the camp, along the beach, towards the tree lined area. As we walked I told him that it was soon to be my sixteenth birthday.

'That's great,' he said, and put his arm around my shoulder, and kept it there as we walked along the grass verge, near the beach.

'You know Sean, I think I like you quite a lot.' I ventured, through the darkness.

'The same here. I mean, I like you too. We should always be friends.'

'Friends? Yes, always.'

'Always!' He repeated, pulling our shoulders together with his strong arm.

'Sean?'

Sensing something, we both stopped.

'Sean, I like the feel of your arm on my shoulder.'

'Yes?'

'Yes. It makes me feel secure. Do you think that's daft?'

'No, no I don't. Not a bit of it.'

'You wouldn't just say that, would you?'

Taking both my shoulders in his outstretched hands he turned me to face him, searching my face. It was ages before he spoke.

'Richie, tell me, say it.'

I fumbled for words.

'It's just that I... I just like.... I like your arms... I like your...'

Pulling me into his arms he wrapped me in them and said,

'And do you like this?'

'Yes.' I confessed, into his neck, as his hands stroked my back.

'Then you must surely like this.' His lips brushed my own neck in a tentative kiss.

'Yes.'

'What else, what else do you like?' He whispered into my ear.

'You, I like you.'

'Tell me? Tell me what you like.'

'Sean...' I fumbled.

'Tell me. I want to hear you say it. Be brave.' He said, kissing my neck again.

'I'd like...'

125

'Yes, tell me. Let me please you. Tell me.'

'I'd like to put my hands...'

'...Where?'

'On your chest, on your bare chest.'

'Then you shall.' He whispered.

Taking his arms from around me but keeping his face buried into my neck with kisses, he slipped off his battle dress coat and pulled his necktie off.

'You do it. Unfasten the buttons.' He said, taking charge of the situation.

My hands obeyed willingly as slowly each button came loose.

'Now take it off.'

I trembled as my hands slipped the shirt from his trousers and shoulders and let it fall to the ground behind him.

'Touch me.' His young voice commanded.

The feel of his smooth bare skin was electrifying. As I explored his naked torso with my hands he kicked off his shoes and raising each leg in turn, behind him, he pulled off his socks.

'Kneel down.'

His hands guided me so that I was kneeling before him.

'Unfasten the belt. I know what you like, don't I?' He said firmly.

I nodded my head. His belt came loose and hung open below his firm flat belly.

'Stand up.'

I stood and faced my beautiful friend.

'Take all your clothes off. I want you as naked as the day you were born.'

He leaned forward as he spoke. His lips brush against mine. I began to undress in the same order that his clothes had come off. When I got to the trousers I hesitated.

'Take them off, now.'

I obeyed and stood before him in my underpants.

'And those, I said completely naked.'

There was but one way to be in the hands of such a firm and beautiful boy who knew exactly what he was doing. I slipped the underpants off and stood stark naked before him. My erection standing upright.

'Kneel down.'

I knelt.

'Take my trousers off.'

They slipped down his hairless legs easily and he stepped out of them. My face, now directly in line with the bulge in his underpants, began to get hot. The cool air around us sending sensations through my body.

'Do you want to take them down?'

'Yes.' Was all I could say.

'Then ask me. I want to hear you ask.'

I felt my erection pulse and I heard myself fumble for words as my hands approached his narrow waist.

'Ask!'

'May I remove your underpants?'

'Yes, slide them off. Make me as naked as you.'

My hands slipped inside the top of the elastic band and down they came. He was magnificent. His naked pride a sheer joy to see. I helped them off his ankles and my face touched his bouncing erection. I needed no further instructions to know what he wanted. I took him in my mouth and sucked. We fell to the grass below us and his mouth followed the actions of mine in a joint unified exploration of licking and sucking. We rolled on top of each other, kissing, feeling, touching. Limbs entwined our proud boy erections, slipping over each other's smooth flesh as though oiled. In great spirting triumph we exploded over each other and pulsed our unashamed boyhood in natural unity, each with the other. We lay, untalking on the grass for another half hour, just holding each other, content.

Afterwards, I asked him where he'd learned to take charge so effectively. He said, 'back home'. And went on to explain that an older boy at school had taught him by doing the same thing.

'Whatever he said I had to do. It got real horny. Did you enjoy it?'

'Are you kidding? It was wonderful! When can we do it again?'

He laughed, and said, 'I'll let you know, okay?'

'Okay, whatever you say.' I agreed.

'Good, you're learning fast.'

I'd come across many a punter who liked to be dominated, and I'd usually played out the scene for them without really getting much from it myself. Now, however, in the hands of a beautiful sixteen year old boy I'd been allowed to explore, without threat or judgement, that part of my sexual self which cried out to be in the non-initiating role. Someone else's sexual energy and imagination,when one feels safe is, I'd discovered, well worth exploring.

As the weeks were clocked up so I learned the art of setting and serving at table. Silver service is indeed a great art. I learned too how to march and attend church parade on Sundays. With increasing confidence I learned how to tease the boys from new intakes. And with more and more practice Sean and I learned how to construct the most

127

marvellous sexual games. It was in the third week that I received my first letter. It was from Tennis John and contained a letter from Singapore. I decided to save the letter from Singapore and read the note from John first.

My dear boy,

Do forgive me. I pray that you are able to do so. I was visited yesterday by two gentlemen who demanded to know all about you. Naturally, I refused and asked them to leave. They, being the gentlemen they were, told me to shut up. Can you imagine it? It unfolded that they intended to let my predilections be widely known in the right places unless I agreed to play ball. My dear boy, what could I do? I told them what they wanted to know of your 'activities' around the West End. They left, having pushed me around a little, telling me to keep my nose clean. They now know, thanks to my cowardice, where you are. Of one thing I'm sure, they most certainly were not policemen. Can you forgive me? I trust, in my fear, that I have not done you harm?

Yours ever, John.

I was baffled. Who could they be? It hit me like a bolt from the blue! The brothers grim perhaps. Why would they want to know about me? That episode in Actor's flat was ages ago, and they couldn't be that sure I'd been part of it, could they? Besides, why make such a fuss to find me now? I figured I'd found out soon enough and thrust the note into my pocket. The other letter was more important right now:

My Dear Richie,

I cannot believe that you haven't answered my last letter. Is there something wrong? There must be. I can feel it. Could it be that letters take this long to arrive from England? Please write. Please let me know how you are. I'm working hard on the code and will forward a copy very soon. Just write and let me know that you are alive. A postcard will do. I ache to hear from you. I love you so very much. Is it all so impossible for us? Write soon my precious love.

Your very own, Alexander.

The sheer pain in knowing that he hadn't received my letter tore through my very body and grabbed a choking hold on my heart, squeezing. What torture was this? I wrote back there and then and posted two separate copies. I also wrote to John telling him that he'd done the only thing he could under the circumstances. I could but wait. Wait to see if the brothers grim arrived. Wait to see if Alexander received my letters.

In my anger and pain I pushed a boy out of my way as I entered the latrine and within seconds found myself involved in a fight. The noise of which brought not only other boys to spectate but an instructor, who informed us that we'd have to fight it out in the ring that evening. That suited me just fine. Unfortunately, it suited the other boy just as well. We were set for a classic fight. A boy from Glasgow and a boy from Liverpool.

When evening arrived, I'd long since realised how foolish I'd been and half an hour before the fight was due to take place, I offered the hand of friendship to the other boy. The mistake being that I did so in sight of everyone else. The boy had no choice but to tell me to piss off. He called me chicken and told me that he was going to beat the shit out of me. I believed him. I turned to Sean for support, but he simply said; 'You can take him, if you've a mind to.'

The fight was to be 3 three minute rounds. Under the careful eye of an instructor we were both kitted out and made our way into the gym. I was terrified of being shown up in front of five hundred boys. It was this fear more than anything which helped the adrenalin flow. If this kid could actually box then I was sunk. If, like most of the fights which took place, we were both novices, then I had a chance. When the first bell sounded the other kid flew out of his corner and planted me one on the side of my head. It hurt like hell. The next punch landed in my gut and I doubled up in pain. Fortunately, I saw the next one coming and stepped to one side. The kid hit thin air. Five hundred voices were screaming for blood. The next punch provided that. He jabbed a straight left, right into my face. Blood poured from my nose and the kid grinned in triumph. Pride, fear, anger all mixed into one emotion sent shock waves through my system. The bell sounded and I went to the wrong corner. An instructor called me to the right corner and said,

'You can hit him back you know, it's in the rules.'

I was furious and exploded back at him,

'Fuck you! What the fuck do you think I'm trying to do? Dance with him, or what? He's not my type.'

The instructor roared laughing and rubbed a wet cloth over my face.

'Save it for him, son. If you don't hit him this round he'll flatten you.'

The bell sounded and the instructor pushed me forward. Back in my school days I'd been used to fighting with my head, my feet or with some kind of weapon. This was a whole new ball game. The kid came at me just as he had in the first round. Punch after punch landed on my body and face. I hung on to him to get a breather and he called me a chicken. Our faces just inches from each other and he called me a chicken! I slipped and accidentally butted him. A small wound opened just above his left eye and pain filled his face. For a fraction of second he looked away from me to the instructor. At that point I belted him in the gut, then the face. This time he hung on. Heads clashed again. He pulled away. I landed him one under the rib cage and followed that with one to the open wound. The bell sounded and this time I went to the right corner. The instructor said nothing this time. He just rubbed my face with the towel. I did not want to lose. I'd had enough of losing!

One round each. The third would decide things. We went for each other for all we were worth. Fists flew. Heads clashed, elbows were thrown in. This was the kind of fighting I'd grown up with. No doubt the other kid felt just as much at home. We gave eveything we could and when the bell went we didn't hear it for the noise in the gym. We were pulled apart and both our hands were held aloft. It was a draw. I looked to the other kid and he grinned. I grinned back. It had been a good fight. It was a result both of us could live with. I discovered later that his name was Tam. We became good friends.

It's strange after a fight the way one can talk to the very person you've been fighting with. It's like the kind of honesty one has with a lover after making the most perfect love. He told me all about himself and his family. I told Tam that I was homosexual. It just came out. His response was,

'Are you sure? You don't look like one and you sure as hell don't fight like one!'

'I'm sure, believe me. And anyway what does one look like?'

He laughed, punched me on the arm in a gesture of total acceptance and said, 'Like you I suppose.'

He kept my secret and we had no need to refer to it ever again. He was who he was and I was who I was, we could accept each other.

Sean thought it unwise to trust Tam with such information and was concerned that I had mentioned him. I assured him that I would never do such a thing and he apologised on the spot.

As a build-up to my birthday, which was due in two days' time, Sean

130

told me to meet him at our usual place after lights out. He planned to entertain me as I'd never been entertained before, and then on my birthday he had a special plan. I was delighted and turned up early.

A light mist of a fog hung over the river Severn and partly obscured the railway bridge which stood on its great Victorian iron legs. The bridge spanned the mile wide river in great iron splendour. We had crossed it on the train weeks ealier. The great flat exspanse of the fast flowing river had risen and fallen beneath the bridge for almost a hundred years. It was a majestic sight. While I waited for Sean I sat looking at it and marvelled at the engineers who'd built it. When Sean arrived, he sensed the moment and sat with me, looking at the bridge. There was no need for words. Sometimes one should just look and experience. It was one of those moments. We sat silently and smoked. The cool night air took our smoke upwards and away in the breeze, where it joined the thickening fog and became one with it. In a strange way I was reminded of the time I'd sat with Joker and Biker in the kitchen of the flat in Earl's Court; when Biker became all tense and said that someone was walking across his grave? There seemed no sense to such a feeling, so in order to rid myself of it I turned my attentions to Sean. He responded by outlining the night's sexual game, which turned me on instantly.

I was to go into the moon drenched woods and take my clothes off. He would follow clothed, but remain in hiding. Seeing me naked he would follow and watch me wanking. Then, at the point of my heightened pleasure, brought about through me enjoying the music of masturbation, and indicated by laying down in the damp grass, he would emerge from hiding and I would then have to do whatever he said. His imagination alone was enough to turn me on. His beautiful good looks and youth were a bonus. I felt his eyes on me as I took my clothes off, folded them carefully and went into the woods. I lost sight of him as he entered the spirit of our adventure and hid. I knew he was there, that he could see me, but I couldn't see him. It was electric. When he eventually came to me he brought his tremendous freedom with him and we had wonderful sex.

The game lasted for a good hour and we had great fun. Afterwards we sat and talked about the plans for the following evening. We laughed and smoked until we could laugh no more. Taking my hand, we walked back along the beach towards the camp.

Suddenly, like a voice from hell, there came a rumbling screeching explosion through the fog from the direction of the railway bridge. A flash lit the sky and a further explosion shook the river bank. In the light of the flash we saw two ships locked together under the bridge. Two giant spans of the bridge crashed through the air and buried themselves in the river bed. The ships were oil tankers and their cargo gushed out of their bellies like the guts of disembowelled victims. Flames engulfed the surface of the water and began to spread in every direction. Carried by the wind and tide, the flaming oil slick tore its way across the river as if it itself was trying to escape the carnage. Sean and I froze. We heard voices screaming and saw men leaping from the sinking vessels into the inferno. It was horrible, horrible. We began to run. Running seemed to make sense. We headed for our training ship.

When we arrived, other boys, hundreds of other boys were there, in various states of dress, most in pyjamas. The pained voices of the victims carried to us all too easily through the night. Agonising voices called for help. Without thought or plan dozens of us (or was it hundreds?) lifted a lifeboat out of the dock and threw it into the river. The arrival of an instructor probably saved many lives. He ordered that not one person should get into the boat. We screamed abuse at him. He screamed back and by the time the last words came out of his mouth the lifeboat was engulfed in flames. Within minutes it was gone. Gone too were the screams from the river. For about ten minutes no one spoke. All eyes were held by the merciless flames. I hung on to Sean, who like myself was crying. I dared to look at the hundreds of other boys and saw that every last one of them was doing the same thing, crying. Some had sunk to their knees, some prayed openly. Some, like Sean and I, hung on to their special friends. Instructors arrived with other boys and they too could do no other than let their tears fall.

The horror of that night will live with me always. We learned the following day that of the five lost was a seventeen year old boy by the name of Malcolm Hart. The two ships had crashed into each other and then into the bridge. The first ship, The Arkendale, was carrying 295 tons of crude oil, while The Westdale was carrying 320 tons of petrol. A deadly combination.

There was no laughter or fighting now. It was all we could to simply speak with each other. The experience of being part of five hundred boys, all suffering with shocked depression was not something I'd wish upon anyone. For my remaining time in training it was not uncommon for a boy to suddenly burst into tears. No one teased or said anything. Arms would go around shoulders in support. My birthday came and went without celebration. I never even noticed.

Shortly after this we ended our training. I said my goodbyes to Sean and we promised, without much conviction, to keep in touch with each other. Tam hugged me richly at the station. Touching was no longer taboo. Grief takes taboos and knocks them for six. I had, by this stage, completely forgotten the two men who had called upon Tennis John. The second letter from Alexander had arrived two days after the disaster. He still hadn't received any of my mail. It seemed unimportant now. Besides, I was to head for Liverpool and hopefully, if there was a vacancy, a Blue Funnel ship bound for the far east, and Singapore.

The thought of returning, almost a year to the day, to the city I'd imagined I'd left for ever, sent shivers down my spine. I guessed the main cause of the shiver was a kind of fear that I'd be somehow going back in time. Going back to a drunken father who'd beat me black and blue with his belt. But the year away had changed me. Gone was the victim, returning was the survivor. Gone was the kid unsure of who he was, returning was a youth quite sure he was homosexual. Gone was the kid who hid inside his own imagination, returning was a youth convinced that in time he'd write.

Nonetheless, the fear of going back in time did freak me out quite a lot. My confidence was surface thick, but that itself was more than I had when I left. There was no way of knowing just how my parents would react when they saw me. I could, of course, book into a cheap hotel and avoid seeing them altogether, but despite all that had gone before I did want to see them, especially my mother. In my rage to break away from my father I'd not given enough thought to her. In the last year, I'd not been in touch. Would she want to see me? I'd soon find out.

Maiden Voyage

Liverpool! Lime Street main line railway station! I stood on the platform and took it all in. Not so bad after all. I looked from the scenes around me and caught sight of myself in the mirrored window of the train. Well dressed, a raincoat over my shoulders, smart haircut, money and a Merchant Navy training qualification in my pocket, two suitcases full of good quality clothes. Not bad! Yes, not bad for a sixteen year old. I walked past the taxi stand and out of the main exit onto Lime Street. Standing in the very spot I conducted my trade from, I took out a cigarette and lit it. There was no going back. The familiar street, busy

133

with traffic, held me there for longer than I intended. I'm not sure if the feeling I felt was triumph or grief. Perhaps both. I walked along the block and went into the cheap cafe I'd often sat in on cold nights. The tea was as bad as ever. Within minutes of sitting down I was joined at the table by a kid of about ten or eleven. I pushed my cigarettes towards him across the table.

'Cheers pal.' He said, taking a cigarette.

'Keep them.'

'What? The whole packet?'

'The whole packet, they're yours.'

'Ace!'

'How old are you?' I asked, without intending.

'Eleven, just. Do you like me?'

'Eleven?'

'Just!'

'Yes, I like you. The point is do you like yourself?'

'You what?'

'Forget it. What's your name?'

'They call me Rod.'

'But that's not your real name, right?'

'Everyone calls me Rod. So you *like* me then?'

'Everyone?'

'Everyone around here, anyway.'

'How much?'

'You what?'

'How much?'

'Oh, yea. I knew you liked me. Two quid?'

'Two quid?'

'Yea, I need the money see...'

'Save it, Rod.' I said, opening my wallet. Taking two one pound notes I slid them across the table to the reflection of my younger self. The kid grabbed the money and thrust the notes into his pockets, then looked to me for the next move. This is the point when the punter either takes you home or to the nearest public toilet. I stood and said;

'You take care of yourself, Rod. You hear.'

The kid looked confused as I walked out of the cafe and put my arm up for a taxi. I waved to him from the taxi and he smiled a huge warm smile. Will Liverpool ever change? I doubt it. While the poverty is there, so there will be drunken abusive fathers and men with money to buy the kids no one else wants. When all else fails there is always sex to fall back upon, right? I mean, when you've got nothing else to sell, then there's always sex. Everyone needs that, right? I said a silent prayer that Rod would not have to wait as long as I had to get some personal pleasure from sex. I hoped he'd be one of the lucky ones and escape street life before it ravaged him completely. How much of his real self would survive?

When the taxi turned off Stanley Road into Hertford Road my heart began to race. The driver asked me,

'What number?'

I had to gulp for air before I could speak.

'Forty-eight.'

The cab stopped directly outside the house I thought I'd left forever. People in the street, kids and adults I knew, looked at me and nodded. I nodded back as they continued to look, while they talked to each other. I guessed at what they were saying. Without a key, I was forced to press the doorbell. The door opened and there stood my mother. Her face changed a thousand times.

'Hello mum, I'm home for a bit.'

She froze to the spot and I felt tears in my eyes as the tears from her own fell unashamedly down her beautiful Irish face.

'Jesus, Mary and Holy Saint Joseph. Oh my God, it's your self.' Her greetings hadn't changed.

She flung her arms around me and we both let go. Tears fell in buckets and hugs nearly cracked ribs.

'Oh, thank God. I prayed to Saint Anthony every day. I prayed to Saint Simon and Saint Jude to keep you safe. You know they're your Saints don't you? I lit candles on your birthday. Oh my God, you're sixteen. Look at you. Let me look at you. Oh, thank God you're safe. Jesus be praised for your safe return.'

'I'm here now, it's okay. Mum, I love you so much.'

'Oh Jesus, Mary and Holy Saint Joseph, I thought you hated me.'

'No mum, not you. Never you.' I cried, meaning every word.

Pulling her tiny handkerchief from her apron pocket she wiped both our faces while she continued to thank every Saint she could think of. Had I not grabbed my suitcases and her and pulled both inside she'd have been off to the local church to make some offering.

Naturally, when it came to explaining what I'd been up to for a year, I lied like a trooper. I told her that I'd been at college in London doing poetry, that I'd managed to get a part time job in a small cafe and that I'd been to the Merchant Navy Training School. When I explained that I hoped to be shipping out within a week or so she burst into tears. However, because she could actually see that I was alright she calmed down soon enough and understood why a boy would want to go to sea. The call of the sea was well understood by those in sea ports. The call, though, was not the sea, as you well know, but I didn't dare tell her the truth. Instead, I told her what she could cope with. I went on about the romance of the sea, of travel in distant lands and all that kind of stuff. She understood.

'Your faith? Have you been paying attention to your faith?' She asked, her hands holding mine.

'Yes, of course.' I lied. 'Most of the time, anyway.'

'You've not missed mass have you? You've made your Easter Duties?'

'Of course, mum.'

'Jesus be praised. You know, I always thought you'd be the one from the family to be the priest. Have you thought about it yourself? You've always had the makings.'

'I don't think so, not me.'

'I wanted to be a nun, myself.' She said, refectively.

'I know. What stopped you?'

'I was forced to take work. That's the way things were, God knows. Now, enough of all this, let me get you some tea. Is it still your favourite drink? I pray to God it is.'

'It still is, don't worry.'

'Thank God for that.'

'Where is he?'

'Your father?'

'Who else?'

'You shouldn't be too hard on him, God knows. He's working in Blackburn at the moment. The firm has a contract to rebuild something or another. God knows what. He's away until next month. He'll be sorry to have missed you.'

'I doubt it. I'm not sorry to have missed him.'

'God protect us! Wash your mouth out! I'll not have family against family.'

'Mum, when are you going to wake up!'

'I'll not have it, you hear me now. He's your father and that's that! We all of us have a cross to bear. Your father is no exception.'

'Okay, I hear you. Now what about a nice cup of Earl Grey for the prodigal son?'

Her face warmed and reshaped itself into a huge round smile.

'So it's poetry is it?'

We both laughed.

'It is, God knows.' I mimicked, in my best Irish.

'Well now, that's something isn't it?' She said proudly, hands on her hips. 'Poetry by God. Who'd have thought it.'

It was good to be with her again, talking. We sat up until the early hours and swapped stories. She explained that my father was still troubled by the drink and had become a very sad man. She coped, she said, because she had God and all the Saints to fall back on. Before going to bed she held me in her strong arms and asked me to say a prayer for my father. For her, I did.

Before sleeping, with young Rod and kids like him, like me, very much on my mind, I opened up my notebook and after sitting for a while, started to write:

Liverpool Boys

Liverpool boys arise and throw stones
In Liverpool streets wise and unknown.
Venture outwards smash all in your way,
Enlarge your horizons make England pay.
Rebuild yourselves escape from the mould,
Pull down the city before you grow old.
Organise groups prepare for the troops, but
Open their eyes demand better things,
Liverpool boys, all of you kings.
Bring about change fight while you can,
Oppresion demands we share a joint plan.
Youth is the time youth lasts the length,
Struggle their way, or as boys with strength.

The following morning, before setting off for the Merchant Navy office, otherwise known as The Pool, I telephoned Andy at his social work office.

'Poet, delighted you rang. Did you go?'

'Go where?'

'The clinic!'

'Oh, that, yeah I went, no problem.'

'Have you seen them? Are they with you?'

'Who? You mean Joker and Angel?'

'Yes. Look, Poet things just didn't work out...'

137

'What did you expect? You conned us.'

'I'm sorry, honestly. Are they with you?'

'No. When did they leg it?'

'About a week ago. Both from different homes.'

'You should never have split them up.'

'I know that now. It was only to be for a short period, until an assessment was completed.'

'You should never have lied to them. They're not daft, you know.'

'Point taken. Can you get in touch with them?'

'No I can't and even if I could I wouldn't tell you.' I said, and put the phone down.

The moment I put the phone down I picked it up again. I telephoned Tennis John and asked him if he'd seen either Joker or Angel.

'My dear boy, how good to hear your voice. Hang on a moment...'

'Poet? Is that you?'

It was Joker.

'Joker, what happened? Is Angel okay?'

'They separated us and put us in lock-up kids homes. Angel's here, he's sound, don't worry. We're going to Biker's sisters'. They'll never look for us down there. What's happening with you? I hear you've done your training.'

I explained as much as I could about the training and about going down for a ship later. Joker gave me the address of Biker's sister and told me to write often. Joker explained how they'd escaped and joined up again. I asked Joker if he could make any sense of the two guys who were looking for me. He couldn't. I suggested who I thought it might be and was surprised to hear what Joker said:

'There's no way it's the brothers grim. They're in Spain and have been for ages, I thought you knew. They had a big party before going. The scene's a lot quieter without them.'

'Then, who in the name of God, is looking for me?'

'Search me, Poet. I wouldn't worry about it though, you're going to be out of the country in no time, right?'

'Right.' I agreed, still deeply concerned.

I stayed on the phone a long time talking with Joker, Angel and Tennis John. Letting go was so difficult. None of us wanted to end the conversation. I was forced to when my mother arrived back from the shops. I offered her a couple of pounds for the cost of the call but she refused. I put it under the phonebook. Tennis John had been good to me after all. He'd made sure that I had more than enough money to get me through the training school.

138

I was very nervous at the Pool. Experienced old hands hung around in long established groups. It was plain for all to see that I was a new boy. A first tripper. The first thing I had to do was to join the National Union of Seamen. No union card, no ship. I joined and listened to the lecture from the committed union man. With my card stamped I made my way into the main office and told the guy behind the counter, as seriously as I could, that I wanted a ship that was bound for Singapore. The guy laughed and asked me if I wanted curtains on the port holes. I blushed and restated that I didn't care where else the ship went just so long as it called at Singapore.

'Your first trip?' He asked, trying hard to keep a straight face.

'Yes.'

'Yes.' He said, smiling.

'What about it then? There must be something, a Blue Funnel boat, perhaps?'

'A Blue Funnel boat? You mean one of Alfred Holt's?'

'You tell me.'

'Okay, look, The Blue Funnel line belongs to Alfred Holt and Company, and they manage ships for the China Mutual Steam Navigation Company. One of their ships, The Memnon, a brand new 'M' class, steel screw motorship, is due to sail for, amongst other places, Singapore next week. Interested?'

'Yes.'

'Fine. They need two assistant stewards. Take this card over to Birkenhead and sign on.'

'When?'

'No time like the present, is there?'

'I guess not. Thanks. By the way, what are the wages?'

The guy flicked through some papers with the unecessary surface efficiency of someone trying to impress.

'Assistant steward, let me see, yes, here we are, fourteen pounds, twelve shillings and sixpence.'

'A week?'

'A month! Any problems?'

'No, that's fine, thanks.' The wages were not in the least important.

As I walked out of his office the guy called after me to have a good trip; '...If anyone wants to show you the golden river, run like hell. Good luck, kid.'

The old hands, hearing this, began to give me wolf whistles as I walked out. Some called after me,

'Watch your cherry, cherry boy.'

I stopped, took a deep intake of air, turned and asked,

'What's a cherry boy?'

This merely caused the old hands to roar with laughter. I blushed and got the hell away from them as quickly as I could. I must find out, before sailing, or my life would be hell.

After much effort, not knowing just how big Birkenhead docks were, I found The Memnon. It was beautiful. Before going up the gang plank, I asked a docker if he knew anything about the ship. He didn't. I asked what a cherry boy was. He grinned and said,

'By the sound of things, son, you are.'

I signed on and discovered that there were three other first trippers sailing with me. Two deck boys and another assistant steward. That, at least, was a relief. We were due to sail in a week, on November 20th. That date being my baby sister's birthday. I learnt too, that the ship had been launched by Lady Jenkins on the 28th October 1958, my fifteenth birthday. Surely, I figured, that must be a good omen. Being a first tripper on a ship making her maiden voyage felt right. The ship was mainly cargo but carried twelve passengers. The Captain was a confident looking man by the name of E.M. Robb. I was to join the ship the day before sailing. Excitement filled my heart, at the thought of seeing Alexander.

That evening I wrote four letters. One to Alexander, one to Joseph, one to Joker and Angel and the other one to Tennis John. So excited was I that sleep escaped me and I spent the whole night reading and writing bits of poetry. I even looked up 'cherry boy' in my dictionary without, of course, finding it. I tried to figure out what it could mean. Perhaps, because I actually looked more like fourteen than sixteen, it meant young looking. Perhaps, it just meant, a first tripper. Surely to God, it didn't mean, homosexual? Was I that obvious? Tam hadn't thought so. No, it couldn't mean that. It had to be something to do with inexperience. Something to do with being a first tripper. I'd find out soon enough.

On the 19th of November I packed my bags and made my way to the ship which would be my home for the next three to four months. I felt like a seasoned traveller, an adventurer in search of his lost love.

I shared a cabin with a boy from Birkenhead, who, as far as I was concerned, had nothing going his way. You see, he had ginger hair. I've no idea why, but the truth is I can't stand ginger hair. Despite this major handicap, however, we hit it off. Perhaps, for the simple reason that we were both on our first trip, we were both assistant stewards and, more importantly, we shared a cabin. When the ship moved its way up the river Mersey, Ginger and I stood by the ship's rail without speaking. On the forward deck I saw two other boys and figured they must be the new deck boys. Watching places, we both knew so well, slide past caused me to wipe my eyes with the back of my hands. I hoped Ginger hadn't seen this. If he had, he never mentioned it.

The division between various members of the crew confused me greatly. They were not only physical but social. Each kept to his part of the ship and to his own kind. Officers mixed only with fellow officers and passengers. Deck hands had their section, stewards theirs. Engineers had theirs. A small Chinese crew had a section at the rear of the ship. Each group had their own mess room. That is, a place to eat and to socialise. After an evening meal, which Ginger and I served and cleared up after, we sat with the other stewards in our room, terrified. We didn't have to wait long. We were questioned as to precisely where we came from, where we'd trained. We seemed to pass this test.

'Cherry boys, right?' asked the Captain's personal steward.

I kept my mouth shut and hoped Ginger would say something. He did.

'What do you mean?'

This was enough of an answer to cause all other activity to halt instantly and for all heads to turn our way.

'Never had it?'

So that was it. I was safe. Ginger asked, however;

'Had what?'

'Your oats!'

Ginger blushed and I felt sorry for him. He obviously was a cherry boy. I figured that I'd probably had more sexual experience than most of them. There was only one way to deal with this, so laughing, I said;

'If you mean have I ever had sex with a girl then the answer is no. So yes, I am a cherry boy, but there's always hope right?'

There was general laughter and comments meant to cause more laughter. That was me off the hook. Ginger's silence spoke its own truth, but the others, some not much older than eighteen, wanted to hear it from his mouth.

'What about you?'

Ginger made the mistake of taking things too seriously.

'What I have done and what I have not done is no concern of yours.'

He was right of course but the banter was only meant to break the ice. The others turned their backs on him. Ginger stormed out of the mess. No one spoke. Should I go after him? I had no time to react for one of the men asked me to make him a coffee. I was relieved. When

I brought it, he indicated that I should sit next to him. He was playing cards and asked me if I could play cribbage. I told him that I could and he said something about me obviously coming from a good home. He was clearly popular with the other men, for they spoke his name often throughout the evening. His name was Jake. He was about twenty five or so, tall, well made and had jet black curly hair. His skin colour told me that he'd been at sea for many years. He was quiet yet confident in the way he spoke to the others. He seemed to respect people. I kept his coffee cup filled and took over keeping the score of the game he was playing. He was easy to like. We became firm friends from that night. He taught me much about living and working on a ship. I guess I looked up to him.

The first port of call was Rotterdam. We stayed only a couple of days and set sail again on November 25th. None of the crew seemed interested in going ashore, and Ginger and I were kept busy, working in the galley, and had no chance. I worked hard on Ginger to lighten up a bit, learn to take a joke. I guess he was just scared about being away from home for he would, in the privacy of our cabin, talk about his family. I kind of envied him his homesickness. I asked Jake to get the others to help Ginger settle down a bit. He told me that things didn't work that way on ships.

'Ginger has to make his own way. When people see him making the effort, they'll more than meet him halfway. If he doesn't, then he'll be a loner all trip. That's the way things are.'

'Jake, when do we get to Singapore?'

'In about a month's time, why?'

'Oh, it's just that everyone seems to talk about the place, you know?' Was I blushing?

'Yes, it's quite a place. You'll love it.'

'I know I will. I mean, I think I will. I mean, I hope I will.'

'Well now, that's as clear as mud.'

'What I mean is, I'm looking forward to Singapore.'

'Good, you should have found your sea legs by then. Been sick yet?'

I hadn't, not then. But I soon made up for that. When the ship left the protected coastal waters of France and headed directly across the Bay of Biscay, Ginger and I took turns hanging over the rails and throwing our guts into the wind. At the north side of the Bay the sea was said to be moderate to slight. By the time we were in the middle, it was reported to be rough with a heavy swell. When we reached the southern part, and eventually the coastal waters off Spain and Portugal, it was rough and gale force winds made things even worse. I was continuously sick. Much to my relief, so too were quite a large number of experienced men. Perhaps, in a strange kind of way, I'd been lucky for I was never again to suffer with sea sickness. The worst part was not the vomiting but having to force down food you didn't want, so as to have something to vomit up. When we rounded the southern tip of Spain and entered the straits of Gibralter the sea calmed to a light swell. The Mediterranean brought a further reduction in sea swell and a much needed respite for all on board. This was also helped by the increased warmth of the sun. My first afternoon off was spent lying on the deck, soaking up the sun's gloriously tactile rays. I would willingly have paid the Blue Funnel line fourteen pounds, twelve shillings and sixpence a month for that afternoon's experience alone.

At the eastern most point of the Mediterranean we docked at Port Said and took on board a sailing boat. The crew of which were sailing around the world. They had, in effect, hitched a ride for the journey through the Suez Canal. Also aboard, came the Gilly Gilly man. The Arab magician who produced day old chicks from every damn place you could imagine. He performed for the crew and the passengers and everyone paid him a small amount. Ginger gave him a packet of smokes. We left Port Said at two am on December 5th and entered the Suez Canal. What a sight, when I woke the following morning at six, to start work. The vast openess of the desert. Thousands of men carried woven baskets full of sand, away from the edge of the Canal, keeping the narrow channel clear. We took four days to pass from one end to the other, before reaching Aden and the Red Sea. The heat of the sun was now almost too much to bear and shorts became the order of the day. I was pleased to have my tennis whites. I kept my torso bare and on my feet I now wore my newly purchased flip-flops. I was feeling more and more at home, as a seaman. From the Red Sea we were due to sail right across the Arabian Sea, into the Indian Ocean, skirt the southern tip of the Bay of Bengal, down the straits of Malacca, into Malaysia and dock in Singapore. We'd be there, there in Singapore, by the afternoon of December the 17th. I could barely contain myself.

With Singapore set firmly in my sights I took to my daily work with a contented soul. I rose at just before six every morning and sang my way through the fourteen hour working day. My high spirits even had an effect on Ginger, who was now making an effort to be part of the crew. I sang Liverpool folk songs and songs from Ireland. The chief cook and the baker, knowing most of them, joined in and we sang loud and long. When I made up my own songs they laughed, but soon picked up the words. This was the song which helped break the ice for Ginger:

I'm a cherry boy, I'm a cherry boy,
I'm a long ways from home;
And if you don't like me then leave me alone.
I'll wank when I need to,
I'll wank when I don't;
And if Ginger don't laugh soon I'll cut his damn throat.

This song, with its other many verses, each one aimed at a particular person, became a hit and whenever there was a party I'd be forced to sing it. A party could happen at any time aboard ship and was just a way of breaking the never ending cycle of work. Jake kept an eye on us younger ones and allowed us to drink only a small amount. Making up songs was just an outward acceptable means of meeting my increasing inner need to write poems and short stories. So it was that I came to write in front of the other members of the crew, who believed me to be working on just another dirty song. My notebooks became my prize possessions, and I guess they still are.

As we headed out of the Indian Ocean into the Bay of Bengal the weather was perfect and the spirit aboard was great. Clad only in my shorts and flip-flops I was in the galley making coffee. This meant working with some dozen or more coffee pots. I lined them up as I'd done every day and poured the boiling water into them. What happened next took everyone in the galley by complete surprise. A freak wave, in an otherwise calm sea, hit the ship. The ship rose in the swell, then dropped straight down with a thud which shook through the full length of the ship. The coffee pots were one second sitting there, all in a neat row. The next second they were all hanging in the air in front of me, as though held by some invisible shelf. The baker, seeing this through his experienced eyes, screamed for me to get the hell of the way. His call came too late. The pots landed back down on the work top with such force that each one burst, sending the boiling contents all over me. I screamed as never before, as I felt the hot liquid hit my face, chest and legs. Almost instantly, the baker threw a bucket of sea water over me, then another, then another. I was still screaming. The pain, so intense, tore through my skin and battered my brain with its message. The chief cook joined in throwing cold water over me. I couldn't appreciate it then but those two men most definitely prevented me being scarred for life.

I was helped to the sick bay, deeply shocked, and left in the hands of a man I assumed to be a doctor. He was, in fact, a male nurse, and a damn good one too. He was calming and efficient. In no time at all I was covered in bandages from the tip of my head to the tip of my toes. Fortunately, my shorts had saved that most delicate of areas from being burnt. The nurse stayed with me and talked me through the shock. He was the most effeminate man I'd ever met. After twenty-four hours of being in his care (all that time he never left me once) he told me that I wouldn't scar but would need to stay in bed for at least a week or two. I was horrified. We were due in Singapore the next day! I begged him to let me get up. He gently insisted that to do so would cause me to scar.

'You must lay as still as possible.'

It was all I could do to speak through the slit in the bandages.

'You don't understand. I have to get ashore at Singapore.'

'My precious little pumpkin you most certainly will not be getting out of that bed until I say so, or my name's not Judy Garland.'

'Please, please help me. I have to. I just have to.'

'Calm yourself pumpkin, there will be other trips. You must get well. You'll see Singapore another time.'

'Please, listen to me. You must understand, you have to help me...'

'...Of course I'll help you. That's what I'm here for.'

'No, listen, please...'

'I'm all ears, pumpkin. Just look at those lobes!'

'There's a boy...'

'Where pumpkin?'

'In Singapore...'

'There are boys everywhere pumpkin, I should know...'

'He's my...'

'Friend?'

'Special friend!'

'Special? Pumpkin, are you saying we're sisters?'

'I have to see him. I must see him.'

'We *are* sisters! Well, they get younger all the time. Who'd have thought it? So young and so butch.'

'I have to trust you. I love him so very much. His name's Alexander. His father is stationed there, with the army.' Tears filled my eyes and I sobbed till it hurt. 'I have to see him. Help me please. I love him. Can you understand? Can you understand that I love another boy? I love him! I love him!'

My perfect nurse held me while I cried. When he spoke next, he did so without the gags,

'Yes, I understand. I know what it means to love another boy. I give you my word, I'll do whatever I can to help you. But I have to be honest with you, you cannot be moved. You must stay in this bed for at least a week.'

'Oh dear God...'

'...I'll take a message for you. I could take a note. He's bound to understand. Does he love you to? Does he know how much he means to you?'

'We love each other. He loves me and I love him. We're two queers in a straight fucking world.'

'It's not as straight as all that pumpkin, believe me.'

'I know, I really do, but, well you know what it's like.'

'Yes pumpkin, wonderful!'

'Wonderful my fucking arse...'

'... Pumpkin really! Not now, not while you're sick...'

I was forced to laugh.

'Now when you're better, well...' He went on, smiling.

'Will you really take a note for me?'

'Like the sister of mercy I am, pumpkin. And yes it is wonderful to be what you are, don't you ever forget that. Don't ever be ashamed of being yourself.'

'But...'

'...But, nothing, pumpkin. We are what we are.'

'I wish it was as simple as that.' I said, sadly.

'It is!'

'It's not!'

'It is! Nurse knows best!'

'I've spent the last three years on the damn game! It's not!'

'Bully for you, pumpkin. Is that it?'

'Yes, that's it!' I exploded.

'So what! What's your point?'

'The point is... I, I didn't want it that way...'

'None of us want it 'that way', pumpkin. None of us want the cards we're dealt. Listen to me pumpkin, listen to a wise old aunty, we can't change from the people we are. So you were on the game, we've all been on the game. Every Tom, Dick and Harry of us. It's what we do now that matters, not what we did. We have to build on what's gone before, like layers on a cake. Now let me get you a pen and paper and you write to that boy you love.'

Like the caring sensitive man he was, my nurse left me alone for a while, long enough to grieve, long enough to cry a little.

I wrote first to Joseph, explaining why I couldn't get ashore and asking him to get the enclosed note to Alexander somehow. When we docked at Singapore, my nurse took the notes and Joseph's address. He returned four hours later saying, 'Mission accomplished!' and kissed the top of my head.

We left Singapore on December 21st and sailed north, up The Gulf of Thailand and docked in Bangkok two days before Christmas. My nurse removed the bandages and declared me fit. The actions of the baker and the chief cook, in conjunction with his good nursing care, had proved successful. Not one single scar. I was glad to get back to work. Those around me, however, became very protective and constantly kept me from actually working. Whenever I tried to lift something, Ginger would take it instead. I didn't really do anything that day before the chief steward came into the galley and gave me leave for the three days we'd be in Bangkok, Christmas eve, Christmas day and Boxing day. I guess I should have been thrilled but my thoughts and my soul had not left Singapore. Jake took me ashore on Christmas eve and showed me the sights. He imagined that my low spirits had something to do with getting over being injured and he worked hard to entertain me. I didn't have the courage to tell him otherwise.

Christmas lunch was a magnificent affair with all the officers and catering crew in dress uniform and the passengers in evening dress. I was made guest of honour on the steward's table and we were waited on by the officers and passengers. Wine flowed like water and Jake encouraged me to drink as much as I wanted to. The meal was sensational and I lost count of the number of courses. I lost count too of the number of glasses of wine I'd had. After the meal we drank brandy and I smoked my first ever cigar. It was somewhere at this point that I heard Ginger say something, through the cloud of cigar smoke, about looking forward to getting back to Singapore in a month's time.

'We're going back to Singapore?' I yelled across the table.

'In about a month's time, yea...'

I burst instantly into song and everyone around me, seeing my rising spirits, joined in. If God exists, he can't be that bad, right? There's always hope, right? At the end of the singing Jake stood up and made a toast,

'To those about to lose their cherry.'

Everyone around the huge table stood, raised their glasses in my direction and repeated the toast. Not sure what was happening, I was lifted out of my chair and all but carried to my cabin. Everyone stopped outside and shushed each other quiet. Jake said, 'Happy Christmas', and opening my cabin door, pushed me through. I turned and saw the cabin door close behind me. When I turned and faced into the cabin my eyes fell upon a beautiful young girl of about fifteen. She smiled. I blushed. I turned to the door and felt her hand reach out and take my arm. Turning me to face her she said,

'You, cherry boy?'

'Yes, me cherry boy.'

'You, good cherry boy?'

'Me, no good cherry boy.' I said, trying to make sense.

She began to take her clothes off. Pulling down the side zip of her tight fitting dress, she slipped from it and folded it across the chair. She stood there completely naked, her arms opening, one leg bent ever so slightly inwards.

'You, cherry boy?'

Perhaps it was the drink for I found her quite lovely. Long silky black hair hanging over her firm upturned breasts. Her slender waist giving way to full round hips. I looked at her for what seemed an age. Could this really be happening, me getting turned on by a girl? Dream or not I felt myself taking off my clothes and going to her just as naked. We kissed. What a delicate flavour her voluptuous lips had. We moved to the bunk and she lay down. I stood for a second above her, disbelieving. Leaning over her, I kissed her lips again, then each breast in turn. My hands explored her smooth thighs while her hands moved up to stroke my erection. She pulled me to her and my body covered her. Taking my erection she guided it into her and held it there with sensitive control. When she moved and altered the rhythm of that control I could hardly believe the sensation. No boy could ever do this. Our lips were held in passionate kissing, my instinct, finding its own way, moved my hips first up, then down. When I moved down she gripped me, firmly. I began to move in, in, into her. She rubbed her fingers up and down my back, pulling me still deeper into the great mystery between her thighs. I could not hold back. I didn't want to hold back. She lifted her hips to meet me. I couldn't hold on. I couldn't hold on. I exploded into her, again and again, and again. When I was finally still, she milked me further with delicate, well timed movements.

I was still deep within her when the cabin door burst open and in dashed the other stewards. The flashes from their cameras blinding us both. We turned our heads away but not before they'd taken the pictures. I turned, furious and said,

148

'Why the fuck don't you all grow up. Piss off.'

They left immediately and I apologised to the girl under me. She held me tighter and said,

'You, good cherry boy.'

She took the invasion well and we both laughed. They'd meant no harm. We talked, as best as we could, about each other. She explained that she'd come from Cambodia to find work in Bangkok to find, instead, a life on the game. I tried to explain that I'd been on the game but I didn't think she understood the concept, or me. Perhaps it was that she thought me too wealthy, being a European, to be a prostitute. When she left I ached for her. Jake pushed his head around the door and threw me a packet.

'It's a V.D. Kit. The instructions are inside. Have a piss, take a shower and use it, okay. But have a piss first.'

After the shower I followed the instructions. The small tube of cream had a gentle thin nozzle which had to be placed inside the end of my cock and one third of the cream squeezed into it. The remainder had to be rubbed over my cock and balls. When I'd done all this and headed back to my cabin I wondered what treatment, if any, the girl, had available to her. Men, passing me in the alleyways, winked knowingly and patted me on the back. I was one of them now. One of the boys. The last one to congratulate me was Jake.

'So how was it?' He asked smiling.

I don't to this day know why but I said, 'It was good, real good, but she wasn't as good as a boy.'

Jake's face fell and I walked into my cabin and closed the door.

So, that was heterosexual sex. It was good and that's the truth. Equally true, though, was what I'd said to Jake. I preferred sex with boys. I was pleased to have tried it with a girl and knew that I'd do so again but it could never be as good as boys, never.

We left Bangkok a day early and sailed out of the Bay of Thailand, hugged the coastal waters of Cambodia, past Phnom Penh, around the horn and the mouth of the Megong. When we passed Saigon we headed north east into the mysterious South China Sea. We docked in the port of Manila on the northern Philippine Islands on the morning of December 29th. Such wondrous beauty! I neglected my duties as much as I could to take in the steamy magic of the place from the rails of the ship. Surely, this must be one of the most beautiful unspoilt places on earth. Heaven sent harmonious music filled the air as waves lapped and kissed the ship. Unfortunately, we stayed there only one day and were soon underway, north into the East China Sea, and the heart of

Communist China itself. The new year celebrations took on a strange new meaning for me. It was dawning upon me more and more each day that national boundaries were nothing less than an illusion created by insular fears. We docked in Shanghai on the afternoon of January 2nd in the new year of 1961.

Shanghai took me to its very soul. Standing on the deck, at my favourite place on the rails, I looked out onto the vast confused city before me. Buildings were being all but thrown up by what seemed like millions of workers, all dressed the same, in black. The colour seemed fitting. Women worked alongside men. They climbed bamboo scaffolding like athletes in training. Lorries, each with a huge gas bag on top which fuelled the vehicles, rushed in every direction, full to their limits. That's how Shanghai struck me, as being loaded to breaking point.

I had to be dragged back to my duties, which was preparing the bread for the evening meal. I sliced all the outer crusts off as usual and was about to load the bread into trays when I saw the hands. Perhaps it was only dozens of outstretched hands but to me it was as though every hand in China was being pushed through the open portholes. It was obvious what they wanted, food. I looked around to find myself alone, I had to decide. This didn't take long. I lifted the tray of bread and walked the full length of the galley, lifting the tray to meet the hands. Within no time at all the tray was empty, so I began again. It was during the third journey that the guards burst in. Hands now gone from the portholes, I was confronted by two machine guns and a torrent of abuse in Chinese. Each guard had straps of bullets criss-crossing his chest, like something from a movie. This was no movie, however. They grabbed me and marched me off the ship. I was thrown into the back of a truck and driven to a building at the far end of the dock. I was forced to stand to attention while soldiers spoke to me, one after the other. I was then stood in front of a bare desk while a senior officer read from a piece of paper. I was then thrown into a cell. Was I scared? No, I was terrified. I'd never before had guns pushed under my nose!

When the Captain arrived from the ship, with three other officers, hours later, I was informed that I'd been charged with insulting the People's Republic of China and could be sent to prison for anything up to five years. Through the interpreter, I was lectured on how self sufficient China was and that the last thing the people of China wanted was the scraps from a British ship. The facial expression of the Captain told me to keep my mouth closed. We listened to a good two hour lecture. They had, if nothing else, all the time in the world. Captain Robb apologised as sincerely as he could and explained that I was just a stupid child on his first trip to sea. I tried my best to look the part, though I found his description a bit over the top. After much polite talk it was agreed that I could be set free if I signed a paper making a formal apology to The People's Republic. Daft as it now seems, I almost refused. Captain Robb, however, pushed the pen in my hand and said just one word,

'Sign!'

I signed and was escorted back to the ship. Captain Robb, far from being upset or furious, as I expected him to be, merely told me to put it down to experience and to get on with my work. What else was there to do? I did as he told me. Two days later we left Chinese waters and headed back for the Philippines, docking north of Manila in San Fernando. For the next ten days we moved very little, staying in the Philippines but moving from port to port, island to island; Masinlbe, Lebuan, Rijang. Next stop, Singapore.

We docked in Singapore at 6.42pm on January 19th and were not due to sail for two weeks. Hope lives! I told myself again, there's always hope, right? I've waited far too long to see, to hold the boy I'd come to love.

I had to wait for three days! Three days! Three full, long days, before being allowed shore leave. I thought seriously about jumping ship but Jake saved the day by confirming that we would indeed be in Singapore for the full two weeks. I managed, through the caring of Sister Judy Garland of the sick bay, to get a note to Joseph, with a further note for Alexander. I asked him to meet me at Raffles Hotel at 3pm in three days time.

Ginger, a full two months into the trip, was showing signs of becoming accepted at last. He sat with the rest of us in the mess while the usual round of jokes were swapped. When it came to Ginger's turn, he didn't hesitate;

'What about the sailor who went on long tanker voyages? He missed sex with his wife so much that he bought himself one of those blow up dolls. You know, the ones with all the essential bits. Anyway, two months into the trip he got the doll out and blew it up. Just as he was about to get stuck in, the doll went down. So, he blew it up again, and again. Every time he tried to get stuck in, it went down. Fourteen months later, at the end of the trip he took it back to the shop he'd bought it from and said to the guy behind the counter, "Every time I wanted to get stuck into this damn doll, it kept going down on me." The guy behind the counter looked at him and said, "If I'd have known that I'd have charged you double."

151

Ginger scored a direct hit! We all fell about the place in laughter. Much relieved, Ginger made everyone coffee then sat as close as he could to Jake. Jake welcomed him with a warm friendly smile, then winked at me.

On the morning of the third day, I showered and washed my hair. After ironing my clothes, a white shirt and a pair of black trousers, I borrowed some after shave from Jake and sprinkled some on my pubes. I polished my black shoes yet again. Checking myself in the mirror, I remembered that I hadn't ironed my handkerchief. I sprinkled some of Jake's after shave on that too, then ironed it twice, just to be sure. I checked myself in the mirror again. Checked my pockets and re-counted the money. It would be enough, for a small room. Jake, seeing all the preparation, handed me a V.D. kit. I told him that I didn't need it. He insisted, so I stuck it in my pocket. I combed my hair for the tenth time and looked myself over. I was ready. As ready, that is, as a boy can ever be. As I left the ship I heard a voice call from the sick bay,

'Good luck pumpkin. Don't do anything I wouldn't do.'

I turned and waved to see my lovely nurse hugging himself and blowing kisses in every direction. I crossed my fingers and held my hand aloft. He did the same thing. At least there was one person aboard who understood.

Outside the dock gates I took a taxi to the world famous Raffles Hotel. Its splendour took me by surprise. Even with the money I'd borrowed from Jake and my nurse friend, I had only just enough to rent a double room for one night and buy a bottle of wine. Nervously, I took my key and made my way to the room. It was two thirty. A young boy led the way carrying the wine in an ice bucket, on a silver tray, with two glasses.

The next thirty minutes were the longest I'd ever known. No matter how much I glanced at my watch, the hands seemed not to have moved. I walked up and down. I checked my hair, combing it again and again. I drummed my fingers on the coffee table next to the arm chair, willing time onwards. I walked some more. At one minute to three I was ready to burst. At precisely three o'clock, there was a knock at the door. I froze and heard myself gulp for air. What should I say? What would he say? Would he smile as he'd done in Farnborough? Could anything be as wonderful as that? I stood and made my way to the door. I wiped my hands together and then on my trousers. The door handle sat in my hand. I had only to turn it and see him. I flung the door open, ready to throw my arms around his strong shoulders.

There, in full army uniform, stood, not Alexander but his father. My whole body came to a screeching halt. He took the initiative and very calmly said,

'May I come in?'

He didn't wait for an answer, however, and without further ado, walked slowly into the room. I was struck dumb, and he knew it. He sat in the armchair and placed his briefcase across his knees, waiting. He looked to the wine, then turned the bottle to look at the label. He didn't approve. He looked to me as he'd looked at the label.

'Aren't you going to close the door?' He asked, quietly.

I looked into the hall. It was empty.

'I am, I assure you, quite alone.'

His tone was not unpleasant. He was not, this time, intent on thrashing me within an inch of my life. I closed the door and leant against it, curious. Having gained my full attention, he opened the briefcase, took out a folder and opened it. It contained many pages. He wasted no time in reading,

'Richie McMullen, otherwise known as Richard John McMullen, Mark Crosbie and Poet. Born October 28th 1943 in Liverpool, of Irish parentage...'

'What the hell is this?' I asked, angry.

'...Arrested, charged and found guilty of committing an act of Grevious Bodily Harm. Held in custody and fined...'

'What are you trying to prove? Where did you get this?'

'...Actively worked as a common prostitute in both Liverpool and London for a period not exceeding three years, before entering the Merchant Navy Training School in Gloucester. Joined The Memnon, November last year...'

'What are you trying to do, scare me?'

'...Contracted and passed on a sexually transmitted disease to others...'

'So you've been spying on me. Very clever. I suppose those two goons worked for you?'

'Let's cut through all this. You came here to meet my son, with whom you have already committed an act of gross indecency, in the hope of doing so again. He, thank God, has not the slightest intention, having seen all this, of ever seeing you again.' He held the file up and waved it triumphantly before him.

'You bastard!'

'Yes, of course, I had you investigated by a reputable private agency in London. What did you expect? That I'd allow you to drag my son to the depths you've sunk to? Your Tennis loving man friend, is that what we call his kind? Man friend? He was most helpful.'

'What is it that you want?'

'Want? I want nothing. My son is aware now, he knows the truth. He knows you, now, for what you are. Want? I want not one thing from you, or your kind.'

'You expect me to believe that?'

'What you believe is entirely up to you. Alexander has seen the contents of this file and, I assure you, wants nothing further to do with you. Do I make myself clear?'

'Oh yes, very clear. You've done everything in your power to prevent Alexander from...'

'...Seeing you? My God, you don't know just how true that is.'

'Why...?'

'Why? You cannot be serious...'

'...Why do you hate me so much?'

'I don't expect you can understand...'

'...Hate? No I don't understand hate...'

'...Why your kind goes out of its filthy way to corrupt children...'

'...Children? Do you really believe that Alexander is a child...?'

'Yes, yes I do! He is *my* child! He is his mother's child!...'

'...And you intend keeping him that way, right?'

'For as long as I damn well can!'

'You're too late!'

'Keep your filthy mouth shut!'

'He's grown up, Jesus! He knows what he is!'

'Keep your filthy mouth shut!'

'Or what?'

'Or the contents of this file will find their way into the right hands. Do I make myself clear?'

'You stupid man!'

'I mean what I say!'

'Do you really think I give a damn?'

'I don't give a damn what you think! Your sick relationship with my son is over, it's finished. And you, you would be wise to see a psychiatrist.'

I shook my head, fearing that the power of this man, had totally destroyed what Alexander and I once had. Had I not been a coward, then I'd have told Alexander all about myself. Now it was too late. It was just too late! My anger left me and in swept a deep and soul consuming grief.

Sensing his triumph, he stood, carefully folded the file and returned it to the briefcase. Before fastening the case, he took out an envelope and placed it on the coffee table. A letter from Alexander? I rushed to the table and tore open the envelope. Inside, in one pound notes, was about one hundred pounds. I stared at my tormentor, for an explanation.

'I'm not unreasonable, I realise that you must have suffered, in your time...'

Before he could finish I flung the envelope into his face, the money fell all around him.

'Take you thirty pieces of silver and stick them! I come more expensive than that!'

There was nothing more to be said. I stormed out of the room and out of the hotel.

I came to my senses, hours later, walking in an area miles from the centre of town. A police car stopped and the driver asked me if I was lost. I must have looked strange to them, a white boy, crying. They took me to the docks and pointed to the English ships. I thanked them and made my way to the Memnon. Once aboard, I locked myself in my cabin and pulled my clothes off. My tennis shorts felt good around my hips again. Was I really as sick as he'd said I was? I caught sight of myself in the mirror and saw only a scared and fragile kid. It was all for nothing. All that effort to get to Singapore. All that training, joining a ship. I should have had my head examined to have even allowed myself to think that anything good could come out of a relationship between a rent boy and a boy like Alexander. I couldn't blame him. It must have shocked him to learn about me the way he had. I couldn't blame him. I could only blame myself. There's something comforting about self blame. The blame, turned inwards and redirected towards self, filters through anger and comes out as good old dependable depression. Depression then allows oneself to hate self. I could never hate Alexander, but I sure could hate myself. I couldn't even hate his father. He was doing what in his heart he thought to be best for his son, wasn't he?

I gave myself to my depression like a good student does to his studies, but with even more committment. I gave the remainder of my shore leave to Ginger and buried myself in work. The galley never looked so clean nor Ginger so confused. When we sailed from Singapore I stayed in the galley, working. I didn't want to see my dreams slipping away. There was nothing to see, they had already gone. I cursed myself for believing in hope. I'd not let that delusion trick me ever again.

The pain of Alexander's rejection would stay with me for ever. On February 10th, having sailed back up into the Indian Ocean, we docked in the beautiful natural harbour of Trincomalee, on the north eastern tip of Sri Lanka. Jake forced me to go swimming with the rest of the crew. Despite both his and my efforts to have a good time, I found myself crying in the water. It's a good place to cry, for no one can see your tears. I swam a lot that day. Three days later we sailed to Columbo on the western side of the island and joined a group of local boys on the beach, played football and swam. Mostly, I swam.

I have little memory of sailing back through the Arabian Sea into the Gulf of Aden, nor of the journey up through the Red Sea. The Suez Canal held no magic for me now. The Mediterranean brought a change in temperature and a return to long trousers. I couldn't wait to get back to England. I avoided the mess and the jokes. The singing in the galley now sounded phoney, so I didn't join in. On March 4th we entered the River Mersey, and by eleven in the morning had docked in the Gladstone Dock on the north side, my side of the river, the Liverpool side. As a child I'd stolen food from this very dock area and knew every inch of it like the back of my hand. It was good to be back in place again.

By mid-afternoon, with bags packed, the Liverpool members of the crew were paid off and gathered, by the gang plank, to wish each other a good leave. The second steward, with clip board in hand, selected those he wanted to return the next trip. He asked me if I wanted to sail on the Memnon again and I said no. He told me that I'd been a good worker and that I'd be on better money next trip. I thanked him and told him that I wouldn't be returning to this or any other ship, that my sailing days were over.

'What? One trip and you've swallowed the anchor?'

I nodded my head and he walked away, laughing. I went to the sick bay and hugged my nurse and told him that I'd miss him very much. We kissed and allowed each other a few tears. Jake, being the man he was, took my hand and told me to get my chin off the floor. I thanked him for his friendship and told him that I thought he was an okay kind of man. He punched me on the shoulder, the way men do when they've not learnt how to hug. I waited for the others to leave and made my way alone to the dock gates. The gate policeman looked at my papers and waved me through. I was back on Liverpool soil.

I looked to the cars parked by the gate for a taxi. A car door opened and a familiar figure stepped out. I dropped my bags, took a deep breath of cold Liverpool air and dashed forwards. Alexander's arms wrapped around me and mine around him. This was no time for crying, so why in the name of God were we? We hugged and kissed and hugged some more. He said,

'Richie, I love you so very much.'

'In the name of all that's holy, how did you get here?'

'I told my father, after he went to see you, that if he didn't let me fly back home then I'd let everyone of his fellow officers know that I was homosexual. He couldn't bear the thought of such a loss of face, and *here I am*. We have a flat, you and I, with the blessing of my mother, in London. Will you come with me? It's quite tiny but it's ours. You *will* come?'

'With you? But, you know...'

'Yes, he showed me the file. I know all about that and I know that I love you, I love you. He intercepted my mail but I never lost hope. I knew we'd find a way.'

'I'll come with you. I love you so very much and anywhere you are, I need to be.'

When his mother's car pulled away, with us locked in each other's arms in the back, it came to me: *There's always hope, right? Always hope!*

also by Richie McMullen

ENCHANTED BOY

In the first volume of these personal and often harrowing memoirs, Richie McMullen charts a journey through abuse to prostitution. Enchanted Boy tells the story of his childhood, growing up in working-class Liverpool in the early post-war years. Brutalised by his violent father and sexually assaulted by a cousin, Richie's attempts to align the warmth and magic of the inner world he escapes into, and the harsh reality of the outside world are increasingly frustrated; till eventually prostitution provides an early escape route from his family.

'Well written, entertaining and thought-provoking, this excellent short early autobiography aims to help demystify and provide a personal perspective on the subjects of child abuse and prostitution.' -- *Time Out*

0 85449 098 1   paperback   £4.95/$8.95

MALE RAPE

This is the first in-depth study of Male Rape ever to be published in this country, therefore lending itself the subtitle of 'Breaking the silence on the last taboo'. McMullen identifies the causes and consequences of this under-reported but increasingly prevalent crime.

The study is divided into three sections: Recognition, Counselling and Research, painstakingly subverting the myth that male rape is a sex crime committed only by gay men. It exhibits cases which cross the whole spectrum of abuse, clearly revealing rape as first and foremost an act of violence, and thus a habit particular to men, invariably heterosexual men.

As both a victim of rape himself, and a trained counsellor and community worker, Richie McMullen brings real life experience to bear upon this horrifying subject.

0 85449 126 0   cased   £9.95/$18.95

GMP books can be ordered from any bookshop in the UK, and from specialised bookshops overseas. If you prefer to order by mail, please send full retail price plus £1.50 for postage and packing to:
GMP Publishers Ltd (GB),
P O Box 247, London N17 9QR.
For payment by Access/Eurocard/Mastercard/American Express/Visa,
please give number and signature.
A comprehensive mail-order catalogue is also available.

In North America order from Alyson Publications Inc.,
40 Plympton St, Boston, MA 02118, USA.

In Australia order from Stilone Pty Ltd,
P O Box 155, Broadway, NSW 2007, Australia.

Name and Address in block letters please:

Name
_____

Address
_____

_____

_____